Introduction

The popularity of poultry-keeping continues to grow strongly, with more and more people coming to appreciate the many benefits associated with looking after a few hens at home. However, there's a lot to learn for those new to the hobby. Chickens, like any other form of livestock, require regular and appropriate attention; they really are creatures of habit. Food and fresh water must be a constant, and there's plenty to appreciate with regard to housing types, run sizes, breed choice and welfare issues.

So, to help with these important issues (and many more), the articles gathered into this unique compilation have been carefully chosen to encompass all major aspects concerned with keeping chickens in the garden. This information will arm you with the knowledge necessary to provide your hens with a happy and healthy environment in which to thrive.

Many new keepers fail to recognise the significance of getting the balance right with chickens. Overcrowding is one of the most common mistakes people make. Chickens are extremely sensitive to stress, and insufficient space, poor housing, low-quality feed and an inappropriate bird mix (sizes and breeds) can all promote increased stress levels that, in turn, can lead to trouble.

Hens become far more prone to disease and infection when stressed, and are increasingly likely to succumb to the various poultry vices that include feather-pecking, egg-eating and even bullying. Having said all this, it's important never to let the negatives outweigh the positives. Keeping poultry at home is, above all, great fun. It's a thoroughly absorbing hobby that's productive too.

There's nothing quite like the pleasure and satisfaction associated with eating the first, freshly-laid egg produced by one of your hens. What's more, increasing numbers of keepers are starting to grow birds for the table too, craving the true taste of unadulterated, hormone-free chicken.

But whatever your level of involvement with chickens, this book is bound to contain information that you'll find interesting and useful.

So, take your time, study the subject, don't act on a whim and above all, enjoy your birds!

Chris Graham
Editor,
Practical Poultry *magazine*

Published by
KELSEY PUBLISHING LTD
Printed by William Gibbons Ltd on behalf of
Kelsey Publishing Ltd, Cudham Tithe Barn, Berry's Hill, Cudham, Kent TN16 3AG
Tel: 01959 541444   *Fax:* 01959 541400   *Email:* kelseybooks@kelsey.co.uk   *Website:* www.kelsey.co.uk
©2009 **ISBN 978-1-873098-94-3**

Getting started with chickens

18

CONTENTS

40

Bird buyers guide

Bob Cross takes a practical look at what's involved in purchasing a good bird – from selecting the breed to recognising a good one

Birds should be active and always looking for something to do. I've heard it said that the best birds are the last ones to go to roost... though I'm not sure I share that sentiment when I'm shutting in!

Domestic poultry keeping is now more popular than it's been for several decades which is, I'm sure, a good thing overall. However, buying birds is never somthing that you should rush into. It's all too easy for the inexperienced to make mistakes that will inevitably lead to disappointment later on.

Treading carefully

There's an old saying – it's probably Chinese – which says that: 'A journey of a thousand miles starts with a single step.' This is particularly apt as far as buying poultry is concerned. Getting started may seem daunting to those who've never kept chickens before – especially as, unlike embarking on a long journey, it's not so easy to turn back and abandon the project or start again. This is why it's so important to get things right first time; the first steps really are vital.

One aspect of poultry keeping that seems to pose more questions than answers is the choice and sourcing of stock, and it's these particular aspects that I'll be considering here. It should also be noted that although I refer specifically to chickens, the basic ideas are equally relevant to other species of poultry stock.

The first point to establish is exactly why you want to keep chickens in the first place. Are you looking to produce a supply of birds to eat, do you just want eggs, or perhaps the objective is simply to add an attractive aspect to your garden. Then again, your interest may lie in a combination of these requirements.

If eggs are the primary objective then my advice is to look for a modern, commercial hybrid. There are a number of strains around and, as far as the small flock is concerned, there's very little to choose between examples such as Black Rocks and Sussex Stars. These birds will be capable of laying about 300 eggs in their first laying season without too much persuasion, and are economical to keep as well. By and large they are pretty much 'bombproof', so if they don't perform then something else is wrong.

If it's meat you're after then, once again, a modern meat hybrid takes some beating. I appreciate that traditional meat breeds do exist, but the true utility-types are very few and far between nowadays. Picking one of these, which basically exists in name only, is sure to disappoint in my opinion. Where a pure-breed is used, and only a few chicks are required, it makes it a very expensive exercise, for the parents are not very productive and have large appetites.

Good performer

A utility, dual-purpose pure breed may fit the bill if a combination of eggs and meat is what you desire. However, the danger here is that strains branded with the 'dual-

Male adult saddle feathers are elongated, pointed and tend to be shiny

and sold without thought, stock gets mixed up and rarely is any regard paid to disease prevention.

Keep your head
Specialist poultry auctions may appear to be a good bet but remember that, because it's an auction, prices will fluctuate. The good birds will generally sell for more than they are worth and there will probably be commission to pay on top of the hammer price as well. The normal auction rules should always apply. Decide what you want, fix your price limit and don't get carried away!

As far as I'm concerned the best option is to seek out a specialist breeder. These are the people who should know what they're talking about. Find one who's got what you want then go and have a look. You're best limiting your interest to breeders who concentrate their efforts into just one or two breeds. I fail to see how those listing multiple breeds for sale can offer stock of comparable quality; it's just not possible in my view.

Look at the birds, handle them and ask questions. If you like what you see, then strike up a deal. This way should save you money; there are no fees or commissions to pay, and you're not competing to buy with anyone else. While this is the preferable way to buy, don't expect to bag yourself a top show winner. In reality, it's very unlikely that a breeder is going to let his best birds go. However, what you do buy should be a quality bird that's been bred from good stock; a good basis to work from.

purpose' tag can end up as a bit of a compromise, offering mediocre performance and quality in both respects.

So breed is always going to be a vital aspect for consideration. When the sole purpose of having a few chooks is to enhance the appearance of the garden, or as pets, then the choice is almost unlimited, but it still needs some thought nevertheless. Large, active birds will damage flower borders with their scratching, so choose bantams if they are to be allowed unlimited freedom to roam among your prized plantings. The feather-legged breeds may cause least damage of all.

Unfortunately, picking your ideal breed is only half the battle because, even once you've weighed up all the options and made your choice, you've still got to go out and find some decent examples. This isn't as simple as it may appear. The common options for buying include markets, dealers and specialist breeders, but which are the ones to go to and which are best avoided?

It's my firm belief that markets represent the least desirable buying option of all when sourcing poultry. These events tend to attract the very worst birds around, with people often using markets as an easy, cheap and quick way of getting rid of unwanted and/or sub-standard stock. I've been to plenty of these events and seen miserable specimens showing signs of old age and poor health. The risk of disease is high too. Even birds that arrive at the sale in good health will stand a good chance of catching something during the time they are there. Other drawbacks of the market approach include the fact that it's often difficult to be sure about the age of birds on sale, plus there's next to no comeback after purchase should things go wrong.

Unfortunately, some dealers are to be avoided too. There are sure to be reputable ones, but my own experience is that there are many 'snakes in the grass'. These are the characters who buy from anyone and anywhere (including markets) then sell the birds on to unsuspecting punters, or simply take them on to the next market. These individuals must be avoided; they are out there to make a living, pure and simple. Birds are bought

The 'beetle brows' over the eyes on this Rhode Island Red are a tell-tale sign of its age; this bird is nine years old

Female saddle feathers are rounded and dull

But, whatever your source, whenever you're looking at a bird with a view to buying it, consideration should always be given to the following points. For a start – and probably of greatest importance – there's the matter of health. Buying stock in poor health is buying trouble. What's more, if you're planning to mix the new birds with an existing flock, then you'll be compromising the health of them all.

So take care to buy only those birds which look fit and healthy. Take some time to watch them in their normal environment; they should appear active and busy. Avoid those that show signs of lethargy, and a general disinterest in life. It's important also to pick up the birds so that you can inspect them at close quarters. The headgear (comb and wattles) of mature birds (with a few exceptions) should be red with a fresh appearance, unless they happen to be going through their

Red headgear with a fresh appearance, bright eyes and clean nostrils are all signs of health and fitness

annual moult. The eyes should be bright and the nostrils clean. Combs and wattles which appear dull and/or shrivelled (a condition often described as 'scurvy' by experienced breeders) are not those of a layer, so should be avoided.

The eyes have it

Pay careful attention to the condition of the eyes too. If they look dull, sunken or show heavy brows, then walk away. These can all be classic signs of a bird that's in poor health, or no longer enjoying

Holding a bird like this, as if you were answering the telephone, will enable you to listen for problems at the lower end of the respiratory system

its first flush of youth. Occasionally, you may also notice bubbles around the eyeball and, if this is combined with a discharge from the nostrils (or they are dust-encrusted) then these are indicative of respiratory infections.

While we're on the subject of breathing problems, listen out for gurgling, coughing or sneezing; there should be none of it. Hold the bird with its back to your ear, as if answering the telephone, and listen to the lower half of the respiratory system. The sound of its breathing should be hardly audible. If you detect any sort of rattling sound, this means trouble, and the bird should be left well alone.

Once hens reach the 'point of lay' (POL) they should have just about all their feathers. So birds of this age which are showing incomplete feathering, especially if there are any missing from the tail, should ring a few alarm bells. There are a number of possible reasons

Nice smooth scales on the legs – no sign of scaly leg mite here

for this, including mite infestation and feather pecking. The latter can suggest that either the strain is aggressive, or that the husbandry has been lacking in some respect.

The treatment of mites is a pretty straightforward matter, although it will need to be properly done before the bird is mixed with an existing flock. However, birds with an aggressive temperament are rather more awkward to deal with. Such birds tend not to be suited to confinement. Those that have pecked as a result of mismanagement should be considered on their merits, and if they are good in all other respects they should grow their feathers back without further problems.

A bird's legs provide another important indicator which you can use to your advantage when assessing a potential purchase. Careful, hands-on inspection should reveal smooth scales; have nothing to do with those where uneven, 'scaly leg' is found. A mite is responsible for this condition, which not only ruins the appearance of the bird, but also causes it a great deal of discomfort. While it can be treated, it's a long and protracted affair that, in all honesty, is best avoided.

Finally, age isn't as easy to determine as health. With growing stock, body-size is probably the best guide to how old a bird is, but it takes an experienced eye to make an accurate assessment. So, in reality, most inexperienced buyers will usually end up having to take the seller's word for it.

As a guide, remember that chicks should be fully feathered with their first true feathers at around 4-5 weeks of age, and most breeds can be sexed with reasonable accuracy at this age. They moult again at about the 12-week mark, and then start growing their adult, gender-associated plumage. This can be used as another age marker, as well as a useful way of confirming sex; those developing V-shaped or pointed feathers on the back, in front of the tail (the saddle hackles), are males, while those with rounded feathers are females. The exception to this general rule is the Silkie, which remains very difficult to sex throughout the growing period. ●

First birds

What are the important factors that need to be considered before taking the plunge and getting your first birds? Terry Beebe explains the vital issues from a practical point of view

Pack them in too tightly and they'll develop bad habits like feather pecking

The idea of keeping a few hens in the garden is a popular one, with increasing numbers of people anxious to source their own supply of fresh, free-range eggs and perhaps, in some cases, the odd bird or two for roasting.

But one of the downsides of this boom in poultry keeping, as with any popular hobby, is that those rushing to become involved are increasingly given the impression that there's nothing to it – all you need to do is buy your birds, get a trendy house for them to live in and start collecting the eggs. In reality, of course, things just aren't that simple. There's a lot that should be considered before anyone even thinks about buying the birds, and this is the important aspect I want to consider to start with.

Why chickens?
Keeping poultry, like any other type of livestock, represents a big personal commitment, and it's vital that anyone thinking about getting involved realises this. You need to be sure that you're prepared to make the effort, and to continue doing so, before taking the plunge. The last thing you want to find is that the whole thing's nothing

more than a nine-day wonder, and that the novelty's worn off after a fortnight. This will be bad for you but, more importantly, it'll be terrible for the birds.

Chickens should never be bought on a whim; that's the first in a set of basic rules which should never be forgotten. The second is to be prepared for the day-to-day work that looking after chickens

properly demands. It's also worth spending some time weighing-up the pros and cons of keeping poultry, just to convince yourself that you're doing the right thing.

While all this may sound a bit negative, I should emphasise that I'm not trying to put anyone off the idea; far from it. I believe that poultry keeping is one of the best and most rewarding family hobbies

It's important that birds are kept on good, fresh and essentially dry ground. Keeping drinkers on a 'dirt ring' will stop spilt water creating a muddy mess

there is. But it's important that those thinking about becoming involved realise that it's not always a particularly easy option. Things can and will go wrong, you can bank on that. There's hard work to be done at times, and you'll have a constant duty of care to your birds, to maintain good levels of husbandry so they live happy and healthy lives.

Time to spare?

Whether or not you have the necessary time to look after chickens properly is a vital factor; you must be clear about this before you start. Domestic poultry are creatures of habit that thrive on routine, and anything which upsets this can cause problems. Owning birds is undoubtedly a tie (holidays for us are a distant memory!) so if your lifestyle involves lots of last-minute travel then, perhaps, poultry isn't for you. Time away from home needs to be covered by other responsible family members or neighbours who will be happy and willing to do the chores.

The 'helpers' need to be trustworthy too. Failing to shut the birds in at night, or allowing them to run out of drinking water are two of the most serious and costly mistakes – believe me, it happens. Of course, you can make life easier

for all concerned by using extra large feeders and drinkers, and you can even buy electrically-operated pop holes which are triggered by ambient light levels. But, even with such conveniences, it's vital that there's still somebody around who'll physically check that all is well.

Personally, I always like to check and shut the birds in every evening, for my own peace of mind. I've only failed to do this once and, on that occasion, I was only half-an-hour late getting out there. Unfortunately, that extra 30 minutes was all that it took for a fox to come in and kill all my large Brahmas – the devastation I felt was unbelievable. Nine times out of 10 it's the owner who is to blame for fox attacks, as I was then. It's no good blaming the fox; it's an opportunist that will take advantage whenever possible.

Right location

The next thing to be considered is whether or not your location is suitable for chickens. As well as the space issue, which we'll come on to later, you must bear in mind the likely reaction of your neighbours, plus any local restrictions. By and large, urban dwellers face more hurdles than those living in rural areas.

Some new housing developments don't allow the keeping of livestock, so check your house deeds carefully. If you're not

Regular use of louse powder should be part of your 'good husbandry' routine

Good ventilation is a poultry housing essential. The door on this shed can be left open because the aperture is securely wired

sure, ask a solicitor. It's important to get your neighbours on your side from the start – you never know when you might need their help. Be warned, though, that an early-morning crowing cockerel is almost bound to rattle somebody's cage. It only takes one or two complaints to the council (especially redently with the AI scare uppermost in peoples' minds), and you'll be asked to dispose of your birds. When it gets to this stage, there's usually no room left for manoeuvre; the authorities will force the issue on environmental grounds, and that'll be that.

A countryside environment is generally far more suited to poultry keeping, although neighbours can still cut-up rough about the noise aspect. However, if you do things in the right way, and care for your birds properly so that they are kept clean, healthy and free from smells, the chances are that everyone will be happy. Then, before you know it, the neighbours will be on the scrounge for fresh eggs!

Enough space?

One of the worst mistakes a new keeper can make is to overcrowd the birds. Chickens hate it, and

Birds must always have enough food and water on hand, and never be overcrowded in their house

they'll go downhill very quickly if they don't have enough room.

If you intend to let your birds 'free range' during the day, remember that your garden perimeter will need to be securely fenced to keep them in. Although the chicken isn't a brilliant flyer, most breeds are capable of fluttering up and over normal-height fences and hedges if they want to. They're also natural scroungers, and will dig for England. So, if you or your neighbours are keen gardeners, then it's doubly important that the birds are effectively contained.

Another potential problem for owners with restricted space is that the ground on which the birds are kept can become a stale, smelly mess. For this reason, it's important to be able to move the hen house and run to a new area on a regular basis. If you can't do this, then be prepared to dig or rotovate the run area periodically to keep things as fresh as possible.

As a general rule, it's always best to over-specify in terms of house and run sizes. Birds with plenty of room to roam and roost will be happy!

Do I know enough?
The old adage about knowledge being power is just as true when applied to keeping poultry as anything else. Understanding what

you're trying to do, and why, will give you that all-important confidence that's vital for successfully looking after chickens.

There are plenty of books available on the subject of getting started, so there's really no excuse for not getting the research done before you begin; it's all about preparation. Also, never be afraid to ask questions. Join your local poultry club or society and pick other members' brains – their experience will be invaluable to you. Mistakes can be costly, and not only for the birds.

One of the brilliant things about the poultry keeping hobby is that there's always someone out there

If you are going to mix breeds then be sure they have enough room and are going to get on

who can help. Make use of resources like the *Practical Poultry* Forum too; it provides free access to several thousand other enthusiasts with stories to tell and advice to offer.

Housing
In their eagerness to get started some people buy the birds first and try to sort everything else out afterwards. This is a basic and bad mistake to make. It's vital to get all your preparation work done beforehand, however tempted you might be to rush out collect your new feathered friends.

The hen house is likely to be the most expensive single item you buy for your birds, so it's important to make the right choice. You can, of course, build your own from scratch to meet your exact needs, or you can convert an existing garden shed or dog kennel into perfectly acceptable poultry accommodation. But many new enthusiasts prefer to by a custom-made, brand new poultry house, which is fine as long as you seek out a reputable supplier and get one that matches both the size and number of birds you intend to buy.

But the fundamental requirements of any poultry house are that it should be secure, dry and draft-free, yet have plenty of ventilation when the birds are shut up at night. Inside it's vital that the correct size and type of perches are fitted, and that the nest boxes are suitable too. It'll need an adequately-sized pop hole too and, from a purely convenience point of view, should be easy to clean out.

Another vital factor is that the birds shouldn't be overcrowded, and that they should have adequate levels of light inside. You should be able to get more information about all these requirements from the house supplier and, if they seem at all reluctant to answer your questions, or vague, then walk away and find another source. Before you buy any house, just make a mental check of the basics: will you be able to get inside to clean it? Is access easy for feeders and drinkers etc? Is it big enough (with adequate perch space) for the number of birds you're getting?

If you opt to buy a secondhand

Making a poultry house secure against wild birds isn't difficult. This fine mesh insert panel does the trick in this case. Notice also this house is raised on legs to stop rats nesting underneath – another common problem for the novice

poultry house, then make sure it's thoroughly cleaned and disinfected before installing your new birds. Personally, I don't like the idea of secondhand units as they can bring problems with them (Red Mite will survive in an empty shed for a long time). By the time trouble becomes apparent, it's too late, so why take the risk?

Avian influenza

Attitudes towards poultry, particularly among the general public, have changed in recent times. All the publicity given to the threat posed by Avian Influenza (AI) has caused a certain amount of panic among people who don't fully understand the situation, and simply rely on what they read in the tabloids. But if the disease were to take hold in the UK, will the house be easy to secure? Any poultry shed can be easily converted to become wild bird-proof. Use of small mesh wire allowings for plenty of ventilation, yet will be completely secure against even the smallest wild birds.

As a result, all of us now need to re-double our efforts in terms of keeping our birds healthy and safe; 'biosecurity' has become the latest buzz word. This is particularly important for newcomers to the hobby, who must become aware of the issues involved, and act responsibly to avoid upsetting those around them. But the good news is that it's not rocket science. We can all make a useful difference – for ourselves and the birds – simply by taking some extra time, thinking about what we're doing and putting in a bit more effort.

Keep it clean

You might think cleaning is a simple operation requiring little explanation. In fact, where poultry are concerned, it's a vital aspect of good husbandry that needs to be understood and carried out in the correct manner. For a start, make life easier for yourself by always using dust-free shavings as a litter; it's simple to use and remove, and will also show damp patches very obviously. It's important that these are dealt with quickly to avoid problems. Straw, used as a bedding material, soaks up the damp and disguises its presence, which isn't

Make sure the house you buy is properly matched to the birds you're thinking of getting

Go for a good, 'low maintenance' breed like the Light Sussex as your first birds. You can always get something more exotic in time

good for the birds. Remember that birds living in a damp, ammonia-rich environment will eventually lead to respiratory problems, and that's the last thing you want your birds to be suffering with.

Keeping houses and pens clean is one of the best ways of helping your birds to stay fit and healthy. I always use Stalosan to help with this

Regular cleaning is without doubt one of the best ways to prevent the threat of disease, and you should use an effective product such as Stalosan, which is a powder disinfectant. Not only will this reduce ammonia levels, but it'll also help keep the pens dry and fresh. It's easy to use, very safe and (because you simply dust the floor area lightly before adding the shavings) it's economical and cost-effective too.

Water works

Another aspect that none of us should ever underestimate is the importance of water for poultry. All birds must have easy access to an ever-present supply of clean, fresh drinking water during the day (it's not necessary at night when they're roosting); it's a fundamental requirement for good health. As well as changing the water regularly, the siting of the drinkers is important too.

Ideally, they should be placed under cover, to prevent the water from being contaminated by wild bird droppings – a common source of disease for domestic poultry, and

a potential AI risk too. Some people place them inside the hen house, but this isn't really ideal and there's the obvious risk of spillage, plus it can create a humid, damp atmosphere inside the house. Far

Dust-free wood shavings are a more effective and less problematic alternative to straw as a bedding material. Shavings are much easier to work with

better to position them outside in the run area, with their own covering – you can buy drinkers with umbrella-type roofs which work well.

It also makes a lot of sense to place the drinker on a paving stone or gravelled area, to prevent the formation of a muddy patch around it.

Good food

The way in which you decide to feed your birds is largely a matter of personal choice; most experienced breeders have their own tried and trusted systems.

The simplest option is to scatter the feed on to the ground and let the birds scratch around for it. However, while this will certainly help keep them fit and amused, it's highly likely to attract unwanted visitors, including rodents and wild birds. Also, food that's left on the ground will soon turn mouldy, which isn't good for the birds and will quickly begin to smell.

So, generally, it's more efficient and hygienic to use a purpose-made feeder that's raised off the ground or, better still, suspended from the roof of the hen house or run. Feeding fresh food on a daily basis is always better, and will help minimise wastage. Feed which hangs around for too long before being eaten can turn damp and 'sour'.

Today's specialist poultry feeds carry all the main ingredients needed to keep birds in good, healthy condition. Nevertheless, I still like to feed a little wheat/corn in the afternoon as a treat. I mix this with a small amount of cod liver oil, which I find helps keep the birds' feathers in tiptop condition. However, you need to be careful with this sort of treat, as too much wheat will slow down laying performance.

Supplementing the diet with a little split-maize will help to create both darker yellow yolks in the eggs, and also improve yellow legs if your birds have them.

Supplements

Although the manufacturers tell us that a good quality feed ration contains everything that your bird needs for a healthy diet, I still believe that a few extra vitamins

Plenty of keepers use vitamin additives. This one's called Poultry Spice

can do no harm, and add this sort of supplement once a week.

There are many vitamin additive products available on the market, and the ones which are easiest to use tend to be those which are added to the drinking water. But if you prefer to use a powder-based product, then I can recommend one called Poultry Spice, which I've been using it for years. I mix a little cod liver oil into the feed, then add the powder to this. The 'stickiness' of the oil stops all the powder ending up at the bottom of the bucket!

Rats and mice

One of the few downsides of keeping poultry is that, sooner or later, the presence of birds in your garden will attract rats and mice; it's just one of those inevitabilities. Your neighbours will be quick to jump on this sort of problem, so you need to nip things in the bud before things get too bad and give cause for complaint. The situation is perfectly controllable if you take the right precautions.

The best way of preventing trouble in the first place is to keep all areas clean and tidy, and to make sure that all food is kept in strong feed bins with secure lids. Rats and mice will gnaw their way into feed sacks and plastic bins given half a chance.

Hard though it may seem, the

use of poisons and traps are the only effective ways of controlling rodent activity. There are a number of good products available from specialist suppliers, and I can recommend Roban Rat Control Products and Eradirat (which targets the rodent without the use of chemicals).

Perfect perches

Something that's often overlooked by newcomers (and some hen house manufacturers too) is the importance of correct perching. It's vital that the width, profile and height of perches is right for the birds being kept. They must be comfortable for the feet to grip – too narrow or wide will cause unnecessary discomfort. Also, if making your own perches from new timber, make sure you round-off the top edges as a further aid to comfort.

Height above the house floor is another important consideration – 12-18in is normally about right (lower for large breeds, higher for small). Jumping down off a perch that's set too high can promote an uncomfortable condition known as 'bumblefoot'. This is often caused by a penetration wound (choose your litter material carefully) in the base of the foot which goes septic and swells painfully. What's more, it

Correctly shaped perches with rounded-off top edges will help avoid foot problems

Internal, removable nest boxes

can be a difficult condition to cure once it's established.

Ideally, perches should be removable too. It's important that you can get them out to clean them thoroughly, particularly at the ends where pests like Red Mite can gather. Use a good disinfectant for regular cleaning – badly soiled perches should be burnt and replaced with new.

Nest boxes

The nest box is another very basic hen house essential, but one that's also misunderstood. One popular misconception is that you need one box per bird. You don't! Work on the basis of three birds per box. Given a long row of boxes, hens will choose one or two favourites which they'll *all* use, causing queuing. The unused boxes will become toilets or roosting stations, neither of which are desirable and will simply increase the cleaning work required.

Nest boxes should be in one of the darkest parts of the hen house or shed, to give the hens privacy and to help minimise the risk of egg-eating. If there's nowhere dark enough in your set-

up, then the simplest solution is to use a section of old towel or blanket to create a curtain across the front. Make sure you leave it loose enough so that the hens can still push past it to get inside, and it'll work a treat.

Egg-eating can be a major problem which, once started, just gets worse. If you don't act to nip it in the bud (isolate the perpetrators and don't leave eggs hanging around for long), it quickly gets out of control and they'll all get the habit.

My advice is always to use good quality shavings in nest boxes, to a depth of about three inches. Straw can hide a multitude of sins, including dampness, which will increase the risk

It may look a bit rough and ready, but this piece of sacking acts to darken the nest boxes and improve laying performance

the show pen, but give them an hour or two in the garden and it's a very different story! So try to let your head rule your heart, and make a practical choice that you won't live to regret.

Want eggs?

Most newcomers to the hobby tend to be drawn into it by the idea of the regular, fresh egg supply; it's all very appealing. To get daily eggs you will need to acquire either a pure breed egg layer, or one of today's popular new hybrids. The latter come in various colour combinations, and are crossed to provide both an attractive appearance and good egg-laying performance.

Coloured shells are another big selling point, although this doesn't affect the taste of the contents in any way at all! Shell colour options include pure white, cream, buff, blue, green and, of course, various shades of brown – some of which can be the colour of dark chocolate.

Nowadays there's an excellent range of hybrids on the market, most of which are based on the pure-breed Rhode Island Red, Welsummer, Light and Silver Sussex plus several others. There are several birds on the market which represent popular breeds such as the Leghorn (in this case, producing white eggs). But there are plenty of other choices too, so make sure you're happy with the egg colour before taking the plunge.

Spend a few moments scanning the adverts in magazines and you'll soon begin to appreciate the range available, and the variety of names that the suppliers use to differentiate their birds from similar strains being offered by the competition. I'd always advise buying stock from a supplier that's been recommended to you by an existing customer; there's no point in taking chances with a complete unknown. The better suppliers will also offer a delivery service (for a small fee) and tend to operate through a network of agents across the UK.

Finally, on the subject of hybrids, I must mention the ISA Brown, which is marketed under various names by the big suppliers. Basically, this hen was bred for the battery industry, so it's a top-notch

of ill health, particularly the dreaded respiratory problems.

Which breed?

Advising newcomers to the poultry hobby about which breed might be best for them can be a tricky business. There are so many variables, and a lot of the final choice is based on subjective factors, which only the individual making the choice can really know.

Fortunately, the one thing we're not short of is choice. The many breeds on offer range from the basic commercial types, through the traditional pure breeds, to the very fancy exhibition birds. A good starting point can be to establish

exactly what you want from your birds.

It's all very well visiting a show, picking out a stunning-looking example and deciding there and then that you want to keep that one. But you must bear in mind that birds in this environment tend to be in peak condition, have been exhaustively prepared and generally lead a completely pampered existence that's far removed from what the average enthusiast can offer.

By their very nature, these birds tend to be what I class as 'high maintenance'; good examples are the White Wyandotte and the White Silkie. They look fantastic in

Perches and nest boxes in a very old-style poultry house

egg producer for the domestic keeper. While perhaps not the prettiest of chickens, the ISA Brown can be bought at sensible prices and has a temperament that's ideally suited to the family environment (easy to tame and handle, not flighty). These really represent a very traditional, farmyard-type hen.

Pure breeds

There are some amazing options if you decide to go down the pure breed route. In fact, there are too many to mention, so I'll just scratch the surface here with a few of the most popular choices.

The most traditional options include the Light Sussex, the Rhode Island Red, the Welsummer, the Barnevelder, the Wyandotte and the Marans. All of these, despite their pure breed heritage, are perfectly capable of supplying good numbers of quality eggs. What's more, they look great too, whether kept in the pen or roaming around the garden. There's also the advantage of them all being relatively straightforward, 'low maintenance' breeds. This, of course, doesn't mean that they don't need much looking after, it just reflects the fact that their featherless legs, feet and 'clean' heads make life a little easier.

In contrast, breeds such as the Pekin (low body, feathered legs), Poland (large head crest), Brahma and Cochin (feathered legs and feet) represent the 'higher

maintenance' end of the scale. While you shouldn't let this aspect put you off considering these superb breeds, it's important to appreciate the extra work that'll inevitably be involved in keeping them healthy and happy in the domestic environment. The Silkie provides a similar example; a striking looking bird, excellent layer and one of the best mothers around... but more involved to care for properly than a Welsummer. Definitely worth the effort, though, in my view.

The Araucana is another attractive proposition. It's a breed that's been specially bred for its lovely blue-coloured eggs. The bird is very pretty, and comes in a variety of colours, but it's the exotic egg colour which people remember most. What's more, it's quite easy to keep and can be run outside without many problems.

But if you prefer your eggs with dark brown shells, then you should give the French Marans serious consideration. This attractive breed is available in dark copper or wheaten versions, and most will have a lightly-feathered leg. They can be quite expensive to buy, but the breed is productive and the egg colour is just fantastic. However, be warned that not all Marans lay very dark eggs; it's all down to the breeding. So be sure about what you're getting before you buy.

I'll end this whistle-stop breed tour with the Legbar; one of a few auto-sexing breeds available. It's

worthy of inclusion in my view not only because it's a very attractive bird, but also due to the fact that the hens lay good-sized eggs which come with a variety of shell colours (blue, green or olive). You certainly won't get hold of Legbars for peanuts, but they can be worth the money for their reliable and interesting egg production alone.

Calm or not?

One final, practical point to bear in mind with regard to breed choice is temperament. It does vary quite a lot from breed to breed. Some of the larger, heavily-feathered breeds, like Orpingtons and Cochins, are known for their docile, calm characters. This makes them easy to handle, and ideally suited to the family situation. Unfortunately, they tend not to be the best layers. At the other extreme there are the 'flighty', excitable characters which, ironically, often represent the better layer – the Mediterranean breeds (Spanish, Minorca and Leghorn) are good examples. All lay fantastic white-shelled eggs in great numbers, but are less happy with human contact and, consequently, potentially more difficult to deal with in the domestic setting.

But whatever breed you finally choose, the effort will be worth it because keeping chickens is quite simply one of the best things anyone can do! Just enjoy your birds and revel in this wonderful, ever-changing hobby.

Eggcellent!

If you're after a good number of eggs from backyard hens, should you keep pure breeds or hybrids? Bob Cross considers the options

There are a great number of breeds available to the domestic poultry keeper and, within these, there's a profusion of varieties. While at first glance this might appear to be a good thing overall, it does make choosing more difficult. If you make the wrong choice and pick an unsuitable breed, it's likely to lead to disappointment.

The most frequently asked questions are those regarding laying ability, and while there may be other reasons for keeping chickens, it's probably safe to assume that most people expect their birds to lay a good supply of eggs. One of the exceptions to this is the exibitor, who regards egg-laying ability as very much secondary to a bird's ability to win

in a show pen. Even then, the top exhibition birds will often lay reasonably well, as will the few fancy birds that are kept for no other reason than to adorn a garden.

Things are definitely very different with the recognised 'meat' breeds – those developed specifically for the table. Laying performance and table qualities are negatively correlated; the bigger and meatier the bird the fewer eggs it will lay. Therefore, it's common sense to avoid these breeds if eggs are your primary requirement.

It's fair to conclude that, other than the solely meat breeds, most chickens will perform reasonably well from a laying point of view, but it would be wrong to assume

The straightforward brown hybrids are still the best choice if you're simply after a laying machine! (pic: BFREPA)

Utility Marans; the male is always visually lighter than the female. If they are bred to lay good, dark-shelled eggs, the eggs will be relatively few in number. Conversely, breeding for better laying performance will mean that the shell colour will be lighter

virtually guaranteed to perform well, even under challenging situations, and are capable of laying year-round without the help of artificial light. For anyone who just wants an 'egg machine', a hybrid is the bird for you.

In terms of egg numbers, a brown hybrid kept under close confinement and under good management is capable of laying about 325 eggs in a 52-week cycle. However, if kept outside, a figure of 285 is more realistic. Added to this, the egg size is good; over 75% of those produced will be large or extra large. To the small-scale producer these details may be of little interest, but they are all plusses included in the attractive hybrid package.

The 'brown' is the real star of the show, and the other colours aren't quite in the same league as far as laying is concerned. Even though they produce fewer eggs per season, they're still very efficient. These breed-based types also offer the option of a range of shell colours, from dark brown to tinted, and including blue and white. They can also present a more traditional look, which many keepers prefer.

It has been argued that hybrids are less suited to an outdoor life,

that they could compete with the breeds and strains bred *specifically* for this trait. But it's not only numbers that are important, size matters too! Shell shape and colour are significant factors as well, together with the bird's feed requirement, temperament and ability to resist disease.

The hybrids

Hybrids are the product of a cross between two pure breeds, or strains within a breed. Most modern brown hybrids result from the mating of 'gold' cockerels with 'silver' females; strains of either New Hampshire Red or Rhode Island Red are used on the male side and White Plymouth Rock on the female. The chicks produced can be sexed at day-old simply by the colour of their down.

These birds are by far the most common sort of hybrid, and good examples include the ISA Brown, Lohmann Brown and Hyline Brown. Black-feathered hybrids from a mating of Rhode Island Red males with Barred Plymouth Rock females are seen in much smaller numbers, of which the Black Rock and Bovans Nera are both examples. More recent introductions include hybrids based on traditional breeds including Leghorns, Marans, Welsummers, Sussex, etc.

Hybrids really are wonderful birds to own, giving much and asking for little in return. They are the product of many generations of selection for the most desirable traits, and the elimination of those considered undesirable and, as such, are predictable and almost 'bombproof'. These birds are

Hybrids came in a variety of colours nowadays. This hen, a Fenton Blue, lays attractive blue and green-coloured eggs

Utility Light Sussex; note the good grass coverage – always an important factor

because they don't have the same level of feather cover as the traditional pure breeds. It's also suggested that a hybrid's meagre appetite isn't sufficient to sustain its body through periods of cold weather and maintain production. However, if these claims are right, around eight million chickens are wrong! Similarly, other detractors grumble that hybrids are short-lived, maintaining that they offer just one or two seasons of egg production. Again, in my view, this is unfair as many provide two or three times that service.

This type of stock has a lot to offer. Firstly they are sold 'sexed', so keepers will never have the problem of dealing with unwanted male birds. Also, when bought at point-of-lay, many hybrids will have been reared by commercial rearers, and will have received a full course of vaccinations that'll help protect

them from a range of infectious diseases throughout the following season.

On the downside, however, it isn't advisable to breed from hybrids. When replacements are needed, new birds will have to be purchased.

Standard-bred stock

Old poultry books list numerous breeds, and devote many pages to extolling their virtues. While most of these are still in existence today, many only survive in small numbers. Consequently, some of the more obscure breeds can be tricky to track down, and expensive too. What's more, some of them are no longer the birds they once were in their heyday, in utility performance terms.

A lot of the pure stock around these days consists of birds bred in accordance with a specific breed standard and, generally, these

rarely place any emphasis on utility qualities. If looks are the main reason for keeping chickens, then most of the traditional breeds should satisfy this requirement. Also, most of them will provide a reasonable return in eggs. However, the size and number of the eggs may be inferior to that of their utility cousins.

Following are descriptions of some of the more useful breeds.

Rhode Island Red (RIR)

Introduced from America at the end of the 19th century, this breed became the mainstay of the UK poultry industry. It was also instrumental in the creation of many of the early hybrids. Most strains, if fed correctly, are capable of laying well in excess of 200 eggs in a season, the colour of which varies with strain from a light tint to a reasonable brown.

This flock of utility Rhode Island Reds was averaging over 250 eggs per hen in 2003

(pic: Graham Smith)

Rhode Island Red males crossed with White Wyandotte females produce commecial sex-linked first cross chicks. Note the compact 'type' of the utility Wyandotte   **(pic: Graham Smith)**

Body weights range from around 2.5kg (pullet) to 3.6kg (cockerel), increasing with age. The plumage is reddish-brown in colour, with black in the tail, wings and neck feathers. The legs and skin are both yellow, and you can find single- and rose-combed varieties; the former usually being associated with commercial birds. The RIR is suited to a wide range of conditions, and what's more it has a quiet character and is easy to manage. Encouragingly, there are still some very good utility strains available.

Sussex

Although once common in a number of plumage colours, the black and white Light Sussex is probably the most noteworthy. Originally bred for meat, dual-purpose strains were developed and it's these that are more readily available nowadays. Before the advent of 'hybridisation', the Sussex came second to the RIR in terms of numbers.

At one time the White variety showed a lot of promise, but it never equalled the popularity of the Light. This variety is similar in most respects, apart from its entirely white plumage, and would have much to offer if a good strain could be found nowadays.

Before the arrival of the modern hybrid, good laying hens were bred by crossing pure breeds; the most popular pairing was the RIR x Light Sussex. Not only did this give superior performance (hopefully) in the offspring, but it also made use of sex-linkage, meaning that it was possible to tell the sex of a chick by the colour of its down at just one day old.

The Light Sussex is a useful – although not exceptional – layer, producing 170-180 tinted eggs in a season (although some strains will give more than 200). The body feathers are pure white, but there's black in the tail, neck hackle and wings. The legs and skin are white, and all birds are single-combed.

The Sussex is a hardy breed that's ideally suited to an outdoor life. In fact this is the best option as, if kept in confinement, they can tend to overeat, and the risk then is that they'll run to fat. Weighing-in at around 4.2kg and 3.2kg for mature males and females respectively, they are large birds. If they are fed properly they have the potential to become a good meat bird. There are still some useful strains available.

Wyandotte

This is another introduction from America. The white variety was the only one to gain a commercial reputation; at one time it was seen on most poultry farms in the country. It had much to offer until breeders started placing too much emphasis on selection for egg numbers at the expense of other traits. The net result of this breeding policy was that egg size was lost, and the breed was spoilt in general terms. Then, rather than put right the wrongs, producers simply abandoned the Wyandotte in favour of the RIR.

The White Wyandotte is a self-colour (white all over), with yellow legs and skin, and all birds should carry a rose comb. Weights of 3.9kg and 2.5kg can be expected for mature males and females respectively. The breed lays tinted eggs, and the birds are hardy, docile and do well both inside and out.

The utility White Wyandotte is a totally different creature from the show type, and the two shouldn't be compared. There is still one large flock of utility White Wyandottes in existence in the UK.

Marans

This breed came across the Channel from France, and the variety that we've had here for decades is the Cuckoo. The plumage is barred, meaning that each feather has alternate bars of black over a smokey, grey-white background. The males may be lighter and clearer in their colour and marking than the females. More recently, other French varieties have been introduced.

The main claim to fame of the Marans is the egg shell colour and, as such, it's only fair to expect the breed to be a moderate layer. Maintaining the dark shell colour necessarily means that overall numbers are limited; increase production and the colour will be diluted, and lighter.

Cockerels weigh about 3.2kg, and pullets 2.7kg, and the Marans always has a single comb. The breed is easily managed and adaptable to most situations and conditions. There are numerous stocks of Marans available – although be warned, some are Marans in name only, laying washy-brown eggs. It's always important when buying stock to accept only the genuine article.

Leghorn

The Leghorn has its origins in Italy, although it actually arrived in Britain from America. It's a 'light' breed and its value is solely in egg production. It was once the most popular breed kept on poultry farms, and it still survives as all white egg-laying hybrids are made from strains of White Leghorns.

The White variety is the most common; it's all white, with yellow legs and skin. Both types of comb are seen, but the single is more usual. Body weights of 3.6kg and 2.0kg are normal for young males and females, increasing a bit in the second year. The eggs are white-shelled and, typically, keepers can expect 220+ in a season, although some strains will do even better than this.

Where space is limited, this breed is well suited to confinement, but it's equally at home when free-ranging, though in that case tall fences will be needed to keep them in (alternatively, the wing flights can be clipped on the left wing). Leghorns have large combs and are susceptible to frostbite, and they don't perform so well on heavy, wet soils, If this is your chosen breed, it's advisable to keep the birds inside when these conditions prevail.

There are a few genuine White Leghorn breeders supplying stock. Other varieties – the Black and the Brown – have made their mark in the past, and useful birds can still be found.

The Minorca

This is another Mediterranean breed with similarities to the Leghorn, albeit slightly larger overall. The main colour is self black with black legs. It made its name as a commercial bird, but was also used by the smallholder. It was a good egg layer producing large, white eggs.

The Welsummer

This is another light breed, this time of Dutch origin. It's noted for its terracotta-coloured eggs, which are always popular. The Welsummer is a very attractive bird, having the 'wildtype' plumage pattern similar to a pheasant.

It's a reasonable layer but not the best; where attempts have been

The Rhode Island Red offers another good bantam option for keepers wanting eggs in limited surroundings

made to improve this, shell colour has been lost. Being a light breed, Welsummer males weigh-in at 3.2kg, and the females tip the scales at 2.15kg in their first year.

These birds do well, and ought to be kept on range to produce the quality of eggs that are associated with their shell colour. Welsummers are readily available, but it's important to ensure that the shell colour is good before buying, and not to expect wonders in the laying pen.

Past glories

Many of the breeds that once found fame through their ability to fill the egg basket are now hard to find, or are now of little value in this respect. Names such as Orpington, Plymouth Rock, North Holland Blue and Ancona come to mind. The Orpington isn't much use as a layer nowadays; the breed was spoilt many years ago by exhibitors who bred for size and profuse

feathering at the expense of utility qualities. The large fowl Plymouth Rock is a comparative rarity today, and any utility strains are likely to be very inbred. Sadly, much the same applies to both the North Holland Blue and Ancona.

If you intend to keep a flock of pure-bred poultry, the best result will be had from the main utility types I've already described. However, to many people the look of the bird takes precedence over the economics of egg production – they want something different or special, and where this is the case almost any breed qualifies. Also, any shortfall in egg production can always be counteracted by keeping a couple of extra birds!

The thing to remember, though, is that good examples of pure breed poultry don't come cheap. Rearing takes longer and they are inclined to eat a lot. In most cases, a lot of cockerels must be fed before they can be accurately sexed and disposed of, which all adds to the cost.

Bantams

It would be wrong to dismiss keeping bantams for egg production, if self-sufficiency in eggs is all that you're after. Miniatures are well worth considering. On the plus side they take up less room, so rather more can be kept. Also, there's a greater choice of breeds available and often these are of better quality than the large fowl counterparts. Another advantage is that many bantam breeds make good mothers, so breeding replacements becomes easy.

On the downside, though, it's worth noting that the eggs will obviously be smaller and, also, some breeds and strains will show poor winter laying ability. As with the large fowl, any breed of bantam will lay eggs but some are better at it than others. The main laying breeds are Rhode Island Red, Sussex, Wyandotte, Plymouth Rock, Leghorn, Minorca, Ancona, Marans and Welsummer.

When buying stock, always make a point of checking leg condition – the legs should certainly be free of scaly mite and as clean as those shown here

H. Easom Smith, in his book *Bantams For Everyone*, reports on laying tests carried out in 1952 where a pen of Anconas laid an average of 161 eggs per bird, with the best bird laying 189. Coming a close second was a pen of Rhode Island Reds that managed an average of 157.6 eggs per bird. The food consumption was 3.84 and 3.66oz (108.6g and 103.5g) per bird, per day respectively, compared to 6oz (170g) that the large fowl control consumed. Eggs graded out at 29% 1½-1¾oz (42.5-49.5g) and 58% 1¼-1½oz (35.5-42.5g). Remember that this work was conducted in 1952, when food was still on ration. If the same trial were repeated with the feed we have now, the results would no doubt be even better.

Bantams are usually (but not always) approximately one fifth the size of their large fowl counterpart. There are many colour varieties readily available in the bantam form that aren't so in the large, so the choice is much greater. Most sale stock will be derived from show strains, and will often be those that don't quite make the grade. You should expect to buy birds in trios (one male and two females).

The choice of breed is yours, but always try to remain realistic. Home egg production can't be justified to save money and, if all costs are considered, it's ultimately cheaper to buy eggs from the supermarket! But it's not all about cost, of course. It's hard to put a price on the pleasure and satisfaction gained from keeping hens, and from having a supply of fresh, unadulterated eggs for the family.

Don't dismiss bantams as an effective laying option. Despite their size – typically about one fifth that of the large fowl – they can be great egg producers. Here Welsummer large and bantam hens pose together

The gap between the pelvic bones on a good layer should be at least three fingers wide

supple, bright red head points. Handling will reveal a moist, almost loose, vent and finger capacities of at least three between the pelvic bones, and four between them and the tip of the breast bone (bantams obviously less). Pale, shrivelled combs, dry, tight vents and narrow pelvic capacities are all signs of poor 'doers' that are unlikely to ever make good layers.

With regard to vaccination, most hybrids reared commercially will have undergone a full course of vaccinations to help prevent Marek's disease plus many of the common respiratory infections. It's not essential to have birds vaccinated but it is desirable and, it should be remembered that while the protection against Marek's disease lasts the lifetime of the chicken, the treatments given against the respiratory diseases will only be good for one year. Being reared in small numbers, pure breeds and bantams are less likely to have been vaccinated. In most cases this should not be regarded as a problem, but if in doubt seek professional advice.

Parasitic worms can harm birds; an ongoing worming programme will help maintain health and performance. This is especially important for flocks housed intensively, or in continually-stocked runs.

But it's also vital to appreciate that the ultimate success of your whole poultry-keeping project will hinge on your ability to look after the birds correctly. As a responsible keeper you have a duty to ensure the birds remain in good health, which means constantly meeting all their primary welfare and husbandry needs.

Good health
The first golden rule is to only ever buy healthy stock. It may seem an

Another good 'utility test' is to assess the gap between the pelvic bones and the tip of the breast bone – look for a four-finger width here (less on a bantam)

obvious statement, but lots of beginners make the mistake of choosing sub-standard specimens – especially if their inexperience allows them to be duped by less than scrupulous sellers.

Always walk away from any birds that sneeze, wheeze, cough or gurgle. Likewise, those seen to be infested with parasites, especially scaly leg mite, must be avoided too. Healthy birds are active, interested in life and what's going on around them. They should be well fleshed but not fat. Feathering is also important; if feathers have been lost through vice it may indicate an aggressive nature, meaning they won't be the easiest to keep.

Good layers will be seen to have

Bright red head points indicate that this hen is likely to be a good layer

Welfare and management
To get eggs out of a hen, a complete and wholesome feed must be put in! Laying hens should be fed layers mash or pellets, usually on an *ad hoc* basis. Birds with larger appetites can also be given a grain feed. Hens cannot lay when fed grain alone, and it's wrong to expect them to do so. Clean, fresh water must be available at all times.

The housing requirements can be fairly basic, small flocks can be accommodated at the rate of six birds per square meter. Put out 'on range', hens ideally require 10 square metres of grass-covered land each. The hen house should be draught-proof but, at the same time, well ventilated to prevent the build-up of noxious gasses. Each bird should have room to perch, and be encouraged to do so when introduced to the house. One nest

It's important to allow one nest box for every five hens in the house

lay, the day length should be increased by up to an hour on every seventh day. So, if the natural day is decreasing, this involves adding artificial light (usually in the morning so the birds go to roost naturally). The increments continue until the birds are on a 15-hour day, and this is maintained until the natural day catches up again in the spring. Flocks that are housed in the spring need no supplementary light to bring them into lay, but will need some to maintain day length once the days start to get shorter if a laying decline is to be avoided.

The above is just a glimpse into the essentials involved in getting hens to lay. Husbandry and management are not precise sciences; these skills are best learnt 'hands-on', applying the principles and fine-tuning them using common sense and trial and error to get the best results. If the results are recorded, it's possible to build on successes and avoid repetition of failure and, over time, not only can we learn a lot but this understanding should benefit the poultry we rear and keep too. ●

box measuring 30x30x30cm for every five chickens will be required (smaller in size for bantams).

Mature chickens come equipped with a good quilt of feathers so, as long as they keep dry, they can cope perfectly well with the cold.

Lighting is a more complex matter. Modern hybrids will lay well throughout the year on natural daylight patterns, but winter production can be boosted (particularly with the pure breeds) by giving additional hours of artificial light throughout the short-day season. For a flock coming into

This is what it's all about...
fresh eggs from healthy hens!

Bad buys

Buying new stock is always risky. Importing birds to your setup will inevitably bring with it the potential for infection. If you are starting from scratch and the new purchases will be your only birds then, of course, the risk of cross-infecting existing poultry is not there, but what do you do if the birds you buy are *already* infected and become ill? What happens if you are sold a bird as a hen, and it turns out to be a cockerel? Or you pay for something and it doesn't arrive?

Well, of course, your first port of call should be the supplier. If they don't know you have a problem, how can they be expected to fix it? Write to them, clearly stating what's the matter. Stick to the facts, tell them what you want them to do about it and give them a reasonable timescale to do it in. Keep a copy for your files and send your letter by Recorded Delivery. Don't give up. Write again if you don't get what you want. If you continue to have a problem, keep records and collect evidence. Any reputable trader will want to sort problems out and have a happy customer. Word of mouth is a big part of building a reputation, and reputations are hard to win and all too easy to lose.

Ill stock

When you buy new birds, always keep them quarantined, well away from any existing stock, for at least two weeks. This should be enough time for any immediately threatening disease or problem, such as Mycoplasma or mite/louse infestation, to make its presence known. It would be reasonable to expect the seller to either supply you with the correct, licensed medication for a problem, or to replace the birds. If a bird dies, it may well be worth having a *post mortem* carried out by your vet, if you feel you might have trouble getting the supplier to accept liability. If something does crop up, you are entitled to a remedy. If you are happy with the supplier and want to continue with them, replacement might be the route to take.

Loose description

If you buy a bird, and are told that it is a hen, check with the seller about how they have sexed it. Is it a breed which is readily sexed by feather, or colour for example? When they tell you "it's a girl", they are entering into a contract with you. If it turns out to be a cockerel, they have ostensibly broken that contract and should be expected to replace the bird with one of the correct sex or refund monies paid.

Reclaiming

Paying for goods and not receiving them can also be an issue. When making purchases of £100 or over, always use a credit, not debit, card. This will cover you against any problems which might crop up. If you enter into a dispute with the retailer, according to section 75 of the Consumer Credit Act 1974 – made simple – your credit card company is equally liable for any breaches of contract, which means you can pursue your credit card company the same way you would the supplier. Of course, a supplier may well look after a 'big spender' much better than someone spending £20 or £30 and so this situation may not arise. If you have spent a relatively small amount of money and the supplier is still not forthcoming with the goods after all reasonable attempts by you to get them, your only recourse is via the Small Claims procedure. This can cost as little as £30 at current prices, (different in Scotland, so please check) and so may well not be a viable option to recover, say £20.

Sale of Good contract

According to the Sale of Goods Act 1979, traders must sell goods which

USEFUL CONTACTS

- *www.tradingstandards.gov.uk*
  See your telephone directory for your local office
- *www.consumerdirect.gov.uk*
  Tel: 08454 040506
- *www.citizensadvice.org.uk*
  See your telephone directory for your local office

are 'of satisfactory quality', 'fit for the purpose' and 'as described'. Failure to do so is breaking the contract you have entered into with them. Trying to deal with sellers who will not keep their side of the contract, come to some sort of compromise or even communicate with you can be very frustrating, but help is on hand. If you really can't come to some sort of satisfactory outcome with the seller then you can go to your local Trading Standards office for advice.

Some situations will be dealt with very quickly, especially where animals are concerned. It may be worth reporting any problems to your local Trading Standards so that they can build a picture of how a business is trading. Any action taken by the TSA is completely independent of any other litigation, and would not affect the statutory rights of anyone involved in such a case on their own behalf.

Ask the right questions

Business is all about reputation and good practice. Ask around, buy from breeders recommended by Breed Clubs or experienced keepers. Don't go for that impulse buy. Ask questions of the breeder, don't be afraid to say 'no' and walk away if you don't trust the answers. Stand your ground and don't be intimidated. Keep evidence, use Recorded Delivery when posting. Use the help systems which are in place. Go to your local CAB and TSA – that's what they are for! If all else fails, there is recourse to law, but it really shouldn't ever have to come to that..

Transport policy

It's very important that the box being used matches the size of the bird being transported – the space inside must be big enough, but not too big!

Terry Beebe advises how best to transport your poultry to minimise stress levels and keep the birds as happy and healthy as possible

For many years now, the transportation of poultry has been a source of great debate. Everyone from the Government to the general public seems to have an opinion. But it's far from a simple issue, and is one that's fraught with complication and conflict.

Ideas about best practice vary enormously and of course much depends on the sort of birds being moved and the numbers involved. However, whatever the situation, one of the core requirements is that the birds should be transported with as much thought for their overall welfare as possible. Unfortunately, this doesn't always happen at the more 'mass market' end of the scale but, for you and me who might be dealing with just a handful of birds, there really is no excuse for getting it wrong.

An adapted wicker fishing basket, featuring three secure, hessian-lined compartments with individual hinged lids

Stress and heat

The two biggest threats to poultry on the move come from stress and heat. Both, if allowed to get out of hand, are perfectly capable of resulting in death. The professional, commercial operators move their birds using large lorries stacked with poultry crates. If used correctly, these are perfectly satisfactory in my view. They are designed for the job and, assuming they aren't overcrowded, work well at keeping the birds in good condition. Large doors allow the birds in and out easily (with careful handling) and the plastic construction means that the crates can be pressure-washed and

BOX LINING

The original, old-style carry boxes were traditionally lined with sacking. This was a great idea until it came to cleaning time, when it posed a problem.

A more up-to-date alternative is to use a piece of Astroturf. Not only does this provide a good, anti-slip and comfortable floor covering, but it's also waterproof and is simply removed for cleaning/disinfecting when necessary.

In addition, you can always sprinkle a layer of clean softwood shavings on top of the Astroturf. The birds are familiar with this, and it's effective at absorbing droppings, which helps maintain overall condition. There's nothing worse than lifting out the bird and finding it covered in smelly poultry droppings.

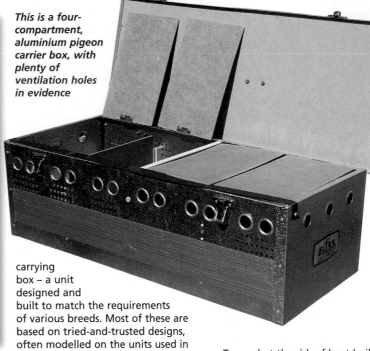

This is a four-compartment, aluminium pigeon carrier box, with plenty of ventilation holes in evidence

disinfected quickly and efficiently after use.

However, at our end of the transportation scale, one of the traditional favourites has always been the humble cardboard box whether birds are being taken to an exhibition or for a visit to the vet. While these certainly offer a simple and essentially free transport solution, there are potential dangers associated with their use. Also, it seems likely that ever-tighter animal welfare legislation from the EC is likely to restrict their use sooner or later.

The more professional alternative that we should all be thinking about is the custom-built

carrying box – a unit designed and built to match the requirements of various breeds. Most of these are based on tried-and-trusted designs, often modelled on the units used in the days when most breeders transported their birds by train. Typically these are built to carry one bird, but they can often also be divided into compartments to carry up to four.

They provide solid and secure accommodation that's carefully sized to best suit the bird being transported. The basic idea is that the space inside should be large enough not to cramp the bird, but not so big that it slides around, can flap, get stressed and possibly injure itself. However, it has to be said that a properly prepared sturdy cardboard box can do the job just as well as anything else, certainly for the time being.

To combat the risk of heat build-up within the box, it's vital that there's plenty of ventilation. If you're using a cardboard box, then simply cutting holes in the side is fine – ideally there should be two or three high up on each side. If you're moving more than one bird, then be careful to make sure that you don't stack the boxes so close that the ventilation holes get accidentally blocked. Also, in my opinion, it's best to avoid shutting the boxes in a closed boot.

Which type?
Of the custom-built carrying boxes most are made from wood, the exceptions being the aluminium, pigeon-style boxes, and the wicker-type baskets. Ease of cleaning and disinfecting is a very important issue, especially nowadays with biosecurity becoming ever-more important.

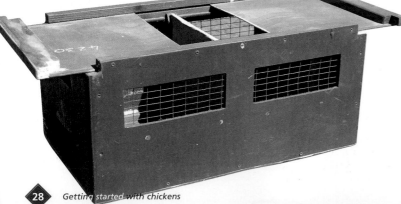

Straightforward, two-compartment wooden box, with sliding lids and wire meshed 'windows'. This one features a shoulder strap

BOXING CLEVER

These are the five most important aspects that need to be considered when specifying a poultry-carrying box.

1. Ventilation
2. Space
3. Comfort
4. Control of heat
5. Slip-free base

A simple, home-made waterfowl box – but not suitable for a chicken as it's far too exposed

Cardboard boxes tied up with string are still favoured by many poultry keepers, but welfare-related regulations may yet outlaw their use

CLEANING

Carry boxes should be cleaned thoroughly after every use. Not only is this a good policy, but it also provides a safeguard against the chance of you being stopped and checked during transportation.

As far as products are concerned, don't be tempted to use a domestic cleaner or disinfectant. These products aren't licensed for use with poultry, and could well cause the birds harm. The best thing is to talk to a specialist provider who will be able to advise you about the safest and most effective products to use.

Prices vary enormously, depending on size, design and whether you buy new or secondhand. However, I think it's perfectly possible to buy a very serviceable, new carrying box for about £30, but the sky really is the limit. If you decide you want to buy secondhand, then take care to disinfect it thoroughly before using it for the first time – you never know what may be lurking in the nooks and crannies!

You must also make sure that the box you buy is correctly sized for the birds you intend to put in it. If you're in any doubt about this, then make a point of consulting an experienced breeder for some specific advice; boxes which are too small or too large are bad news.

When birds are put into a carrying box, and the lid is closed, the darkness inside has a great settling effect, calming the bird and usually encouraging them to sit down and go to sleep, which is the ideal, least stressful state.

Boxes that are subdivided inside really are the best option if you need to move more than one bird at once. The dividers will keep all the occupants as calm as possible, and will prevent any nasties such as feather-pecking. They will also help control heat build-up, assuming each compartment is adequately ventilated.

As I've already mentioned, heat within a carrying box can be a killer, and can strike surprisingly quickly too. So, as well as box ventilation, it makes sense to keep the car's interior at a reasonable temperature too. Better to wear a coat yourself and turn the heater

A variation on the wooden box theme. This design has a central carrying handle on top

down, rather than drive in a t-shirt and asphyxiate the birds by accident. However, don't be tempted to put a water drinker in the box. This really shouldn't be necessary, for if the box interior is dark the birds will tend not to drink anyway. Also, there's the risk of the water getting spilt inside the box. If you're on a long journey, then take fresh water with you and make stops to 'water' the birds and prevent dehydration setting-in.

The pictures included here illustrate the typical range of box types available, their lid designs and the different ways in which they can be carried. My own preference is for the closed box-type, with a secure fastening and solid lid.

The use of the pet carriers is becoming more common, but I'm not a fan of this approach. Although these can be bought in a variety of sizes, are made of easy-clean plastic and can obviously double-up to be used for transporting cats and dogs too, I don't like the 'open front' design. This, in my view, tends to cause panic if the birds are suddenly disturbed. So, if you must use this design, at least remember to cover the front to darken the interior and prevent the bird inside from being spooked by things outside. It's for this very reason that traditional, wooden poultry carrying boxes are generally fully-closed.

General health

Robin Creighton advises on the fundamentals of getting started with poultry and explains how to assess a bird's general health when buying

Eye, comb and nostril condition can tell you a great deal about the overall health of a prospective purchase

Once you've made the decision to start keeping poultry, your first job is to get down to some serious planning! This really is vital if future disasters are to be avoided; I hear all too often about people who rush into the hobby, buy or make unsuitable housing and then wonder why their birds become ill.

Another common mistake made by beginners is to buy unsuitable breeds of chicken on impulse.

Housing

The key aspect to be considered is the space you have available. In essence, the more you have the better, and the happier the birds you keep will be. But, whatever you have, it's important to match the birds to it. So, for example, if you've only got room for a 6x4' house and similar-sized run, then you need to look at buying bantams rather than large fowl because the latter need more space.

As well as being vermin-proof, the housing needs to be well constructed to prevent predators such as foxes, stoats or mink getting inside. Rats and mice will transmit diseases such as salmonella, and will also spoil any food they can get at. I'll not go into the details of poultry house construction here, but a couple of fundamental requirements are that the structure must be damp-free and well ventilated; the latter being vital for preventing respiratory disease.

Also, there needs to be enough perching space for all the birds using the house, so there's no fighting for space. Perch positioning is important too – they must be sited out of drafts, and be at the correct height for the birds using them. Much of managing livestock correctly comes down to common sense. Often I'll put myself in the birds' position, especially where housing is concerned. If the conclusion is that I'd be happy to spend time in their house, then so will they. If not, then something's wrong.

A poultry house needs to be large enough so that, on a wet day, all the birds can comfortably shelter inside it. If the accommodation is too small for the number of birds you have, those at the bottom of the pecking order will end up being forced to stand outside in the rain.

Always bear in mind that overcrowding is one of the commonest causes of problems, including respiratory diseases and coccidiosis. Too many birds will increase the concentration of these agents in the environment, making infection more likely. Overcrowding will also lead to bullying, and bullied birds can suffer terribly. Typically they go short of food and suffer badly with debilitating stress which increases their susceptibility to disease. The situation will be made worse if different age groups, and birds of different sizes, are mixed together.

Handling is vital when assessing a bird you're about to buy. A pronounced, sharp breast bone should be a concern – it indicates a bird that's underweight for some reason

Food and water

As a general rule I prefer to locate feeders and drinkers inside the hen house. This prevents the feed being 'spoilt' by rain, and also reduces the risk of contamination from wild bird faeces – a vital aspect nowadays with the threat of Avian Influenza constantly in the background.

Obviously, feeders and drinkers should never be positioned beneath the perches otherwise they'll be contaminated with faeces, greatly increasing the risk of disease. Also, drinkers and feeders should be such that the birds cannot perch on them – putting lids on the feeders will prevent this.

It's also wise not to place feeders and drinkers directly next to each other. Diseases like coccidiosis thrive in damp conditions, as might occur in the litter next to a drinker. Then, if pellets get scattered over these areas because the feeder is placed close by, the birds' intake of coccidial oocytes will be increased. However, this is really only of concern in young birds. Raising the drinkers and feeders off the ground on bricks will reduce the faecal contamination of the food and water.

Selecting birds

Having completed all your planning, sited your house and built a run, the next step is to choose your birds. There are pitfalls to be avoided here, so considerable thought is needed about which breed is most suitable for your situation. For example, it wouldn't be suitable to put large Old English Game together with Sebrights. The golden rule is to make sure that the birds are roughly the same size – can you imagine living with someone four times bigger than you, who keeps pecking your head?

Some breeds can be aggressive, making them unsuitable for a mixed-flock environment. You also need to get birds of a similar age. A young pullet could easily be badly bullied by an adult hen. So you must do your research and be definite about what you want before going to buy. The impulse buying of unsuitable birds is just about the worst thing you can do, and is almost certain to lead to problems.

Take time to pick a suitable source for the birds as well. Personally, I never buy from markets; they can be a hotbed of disease and infection. It's far better to buy direct from a breeder with a good reputation. Most breed clubs and local poultry societies will be

Birds which fight can show pockmarked combs. While this isn't necessarily a problem in itself, it should raise question marks about the standard of husbandry being provided

happy to put you in touch with recommended suppliers offering good quality, well-bred stock.

However, before buying any bird, have a good look at all those available and the conditions in which they are kept. This will give you a good indicator of the breeder's standards of welfare and, therefore, a valuable pointer towards the quality of birds being offered. Never be afraid to simply walk away if you find birds in dirty conditions, or they are obviously sneezing or looking unhealthy.

Remember, also, that even if you buy outwardly healthy-looking stock, they may actually be carrying diseases. As such, they could pose a serious threat to any birds you already have, so isolation for a few weeks after purchase is always important.

Inspection time

So, what should you actually be looking for when assessing a potential purchase? Well, the aspects I always consider when buying are as follows.

Comb

In most breeds this should be red, indicating good health. But, some breeds – like the Silkie – have a mulberry-coloured comb, which is a standard feature. Young birds can naturally be quite pale in the face sometimes, but their combs should at least be pink, if not red. However, a very pale comb on an adult bird is a bad sign which can indicate anaemia. The commonest cause of this is red mite (a tiny, blood-sucking creature that lives off the birds in the hen house, and 'attacks' the birds at night, as they are roosting).

A bluish/purplish comb indicates cyanosis (a lack of oxygen in the blood stream). This can be caused by heart failure, but the commonest cause is chronic respiratory disease, leading to lung damage.

Eyes

These should be bright and alert. Sunken eyes indicate dehydration, which only occurs if the bird is seriously ill. Also look for any discharge from eyes, or crusting on the face indicating that this has happened recently. Eye discharge can be thick – resembling pus – or

very bubbly and watery. The latter can be an indicator of mycoplasma. However, this isn't a straightforward issue as Indian Game, for example, will often show frothy bubbles at the corners of their eyes when they are perfectly healthy.

If the discharge is only in one eye, this points towards a localised problem or disease, rather than a systemic one affecting both. The most common cause of single-eye discharge is a corneal ulcer, resulting from a scratch to the surface of the eye, or a foreign body lodged under the eyelid. This may heal on its own, or might require antibiotics to clear it up. Also look for any sinus swelling below the eyes – another indicator of mycoplasma.

Beak

A quick look inside the beak, at the condition of the mucus membranes within, provides another very useful indicator of a bird's general health

Inspect the beak to make sure it's not twisted or malaligned. These defects may cause eating difficulties for the bird, and will require regular clipping.

Nostrils

Check for signs of discharge here too – nasal discharge could indicate an upper respiratory tract infection. Sometimes there's no actual discharge because the nostrils have already become blocked with it. To inspect further, gently open the beak and make sure that the mucus membranes inside are pink, and that the back of the mouth (pharynx) is free from discharge.

Check the vent area carefully for signs of parasite infestation and faecal soiling

Large amounts of discharge here indicate an infection.

Crop

Feel the crop at the base of the neck; it should be the size of a golf ball on an average bird. If the bird isn't eating, the crop may be completely empty. Alternatively, if it's large and pendulous, this can be a sign of sour crop (a fungal infection caused by candida albicans).

A very large and hard crop can indicate a condition known as crop impaction, caused by the consumption of indigestible, fibrous material.

Vent

Always inspect the vent area carefully; it's a favourite site for lice infestations. If they're there, you'll be able to see them quite clearly running around on the bird's skin. If you spot white deposits on the feather shafts around the vent, these are lice eggs.

Northern Mite is another parasite commonly found in the vent area. These appear as small dark specs, and can be seen crawling around,

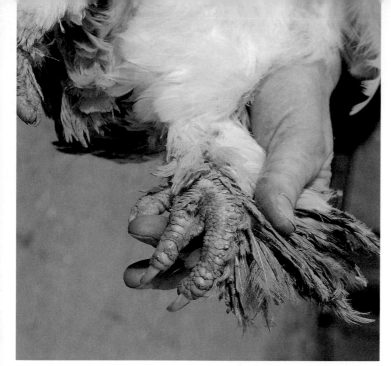

Legs
A healthy hen should have smooth legs with no raised scales. Scaly leg is a common and uncomfortable problem caused by mites which burrow into the legs, lifting the scales as they do so. This condition can appear quite minor initially, but will quickly worsen if allowed to.

Plumage
Always take time to examine a bird's feathers. Ideally they should be smooth and shiny. Gently part them to check for any evidence of lice. These parasites are generally 2–3mm long and quite fast-moving. Some live in the feathers of the body, while others congregate around the vent.

Body condition
Feel the breast bone and breast muscles to give you an idea about the general condition of the bird. Unfortunately, it takes practice to learn to appreciate the good and bad points in this area. However, some young birds – and birds in lay – can be naturally a bit thin here. If the breast bone (keel) is very prominent and sharp, this indicates the bird is thin, and might have some underlying disease problem.

Scaly leg mite is another important problem to watch for when buying. Feathered-leg breeds tend to be at greater risk from this uncomfortable condition

albeit much more slowly than lice. Northern Mite can also be found in small clusters around the comb, so check here too.

Check the vent itself, too. It should be clean, pink and smooth. There is a condition called 'vent gleet'; the vent becomes covered in crusts. This is thought to be caused by a bacterial infection, and is difficult to cure.

Finally, assess the condition of the feathers below the vent – they should be clean and fluffy. If they're covered in faeces, this could indicate diarrhoea. In young birds, blood around the vent can be an indicator of coccidiosis.

And finally...
Of course, if you pick your breeder carefully then, hopefully, you're unlikely to run into any of the aforementioned problems. Nevertheless, it's always sensible to make a careful check of prospective purchases anyway. If nothing else, it'll provide good handling practice!

If you do make a purchase then don't overlook the transportation needs of the birds you're buying. Make sure you use suitable, sturdy and well-ventilated boxes to take them home in. It's also wise not to put birds which have not been together previously in the same box on the way home. As a rule, chickens should only ever be mixed together under close supervision. Always remember that a dominant cock or hen can do serious damage to other birds.

Buying good, healthy birds in the first place really is the name of the game. Get it right and you'll be rewarded with hours of pleasure from your new feathered friends and won't regret it!

Mixed flocks need careful management, in terms of breed choice and supervision, if problems are to be avoided. Beginners are perhaps best advised to keep different breeds segregated until their husbandry experience develops

Spread a little happiness!

Straw is a cheap and traditional alternative to the more modern bedding materials, but beware of the hidden dangers!

Tony Beebe looks into the options when it comes to choosing the right bedding material for your birds – a very significant health-related issue

What you spread around on the floor of your hen house might not seem very important to you but, as far as the birds who'll be living in it are concerned, it's a very serious matter indeed.

As with most things nowadays, there's plenty of choice available – some options are great, others not so. The first thing for everyone to realise is that using the wrong product can cause untold problems for your stock. The breeds you keep play a part too. Some, for instance, produce more waste fluid than others – the Houdan is a good example of this. A breed like this can need cleaning out twice as often as other birds.

Good management

Top quality, well chosen hen-house bedding is one of the issues at the core of good poultry management, and it plays a significant role in ensuring the best egg production and bird health. Damp, wet litter is one of the most common causes of poultry problems; in particular respiratory disease and worm-related problems. When rearing chicks, the dreaded coccidiosis is a major risk, and it's more likely to develop in damp, dirty litter.

It's vital to keep stock clean and dry, particularly if space is limited. Prevention is always better than cure! Sheds that reek of ammonia because the bedding needs changing are bad news. Ammonia is a major cause of eye problems, and can also create burning on the hocks of birds which don't roost on the perches.

My personal preference is for straightforward, old-fashioned shavings, which I consider to be the best option. They are economical to buy and readily available. However, I also use Stalosan powder under the shavings, which helps create both a fresher and cleaner environment in which the birds can thrive, but more of this later. To give you an idea of the sort of routine necessary, my own method includes regular cleaning to keep the birds and the sheds in fine fettle. After removing the old litter, Stalosan is sprinkled over the floor (particularly on any damp areas) and left to settle for a few minutes before a fresh layer of shavings is thrown over the top.

Turkey poults happy and healthy on Easibed

I'm always careful to use softwood shavings, because those containing dark slivers (usually hard wood pieces) can cause splinter problems for the birds' feet. The shavings are never put down too deep – this can hide damp patches – and I aim for a layer that's 2in/5cm thick. An added advantage of this approach is that it's easy to spot and deal with localised areas of soiling, without having to clean out the whole shed. Waste shavings can be used for the garden, but they do take a long while to rot down.

Being careful about the bedding you use, and how you use it, will make a big difference to the health of your birds. It's a vital husbandry issue that people often overlook

Most grain and horse supply companies sell large bales of shavings handily compressed and packed in polythene, which are economic to buy. Always store it in a dry place as shavings should never be used damp. After you've spread fresh litter in a shed, you'll often notice the birds rolling around and 'bathing' in it with pleasure – just another indicator of its importance.

Although Stalosan is a powder disinfectant and not strictly a bedding product, it's nevertheless worthy of inclusion here because it's so effective. It was developed in Denmark about 35 years ago, and I've been using it for ages, both with shavings and straw bedding. It has a remarkable way of drying-out a damp pen, and works against all types of nasties including Coccidia, E.coli virus and worm eggs etc. In my experience, it's great at killing the ammonia smell too, and I'm convinced that its regular use has had a big influence on this. I use the product with all ages of poultry – from chicks to adults – and should point out that it's also recommended as a help with the prevention of blackhead in turkeys.

Old favourite

Straw is probably the old-time bedding favourite. I've used it but only very occasionally. It's the best for waterfowl, especially geese, and is easy to move and can be burnt or recycled afterwards. What's more, when supplied by the local farmer,

it's usually an economical alternative. However, there can be serious downsides if it's not managed correctly.

When used in a hen house, straw tends to stay looking 'as good as new', but this can be deceptive. Lift the surface layer after a few days and you may find a soggy mess lurking beneath, which quickly becomes a potential health hazard (respiratory problems). So if you want to use straw, turn it very frequently and replace on a regular basis. The same applies if it's being used in the nest boxes.

The alternatives

There are a number of interesting bedding alternatives available these days. I've tried those detailed here, and the first is a Dutch material called Aubiose. It's made from chopped hemp, and is dust-free and easy to use. I liked it, finding it very absorbent and long-lasting in the pen. It's actually intended for use with horses, but works very well with poultry. I found it a good litter to use, as long as it was raked through regularly. This was its only downside; it does need to be turned frequently to avoid clogging. It's more expensive than wood shavings but, bearing in mind its good performance, could well be worth the extra cash.

Like Aubiose, Easichick is another bedding product originally developed for the horse market. I found it easy to keep clean, and simple to dispose of once dirty – it makes good compost, rotting down quicker than shavings. What's more, the manufacturer says it doesn't attract rodents or slugs. Wet patches are easy to remove just by lifting them clear.

Finally, there's sawdust. I've left this one to the end because it's the one form of litter that I'd never use now. It's dusty and causes respiratory problems, it gets dirty very quickly and you need loads of it to achieve a useful covering. Although sawdust is a cheap alternative, it's best left well alone in my opinion.

I did use it many years ago, with what I can only describe as devastating results. Anything with such a high dust content really shouldn't be brought anywhere near poultry.

Pure or not?

Dudley Mallett from High Down Poultry suggests that, contrary to popular belief within the Fancy, there's almost no such thing as a 'pure-breed' chicken

There are many poultry breeders and keepers who continue to believe that the so-called 'pure breeds' that we have today are just that. In fact, even the most established – like this White Sussex – are man-made creations, just like the modern hybrids

The term 'pure breed' is a bit of a misnomer when applied to the range of chickens we have today. The great majority of breeds now in existence have, over the centuries, been created by man, and never actually existed naturally in the wild. Without getting into a Darwinian discussion, the only true pure-bred chicken we can safely single out as worth of the term 'pure breed' is the Jungle Fowl (*Gallus gallus*).

Sometimes referred to as *G. gallus (domesticus)*, this bird was the first to be domesticated from the wild, and used as a source of eggs and meat across India and south-east Asia. Many variants were kept by villagers as working fowl, creating a range of sizes and colours which became peculiar to the area in which they were domesticated.

Common ancestor

It's from these domesticated Jungle Fowl that all the chickens of today are descended. Keepers down the centuries have refined and crossed these birds and, by both selective and accidental breeding, have arrived at the range of poultry we know now.

This process of cross-breeding carries on within the breed clubs today, in an effort to refine or enhance fowl, or develop new and interesting colour variations. However, the Poultry Club of Great Britain imposes stringent conditions before a new breed or colour can be officially recognised (standardised). Proof is needed that any new cross-breed – for that's what they are – breeds true, is kept by more than one enthusiast and has been kept and recorded accurately for a number of years.

While the purists among the Fancy tend to look-on with disdain at today's commercial hybrids, the truth is that they really are no different than those birds they hail as pure-bred chickens. Most if not all the standardised breeds in the PCGB's book of British Poultry Standards were created by cross-breeding and, in many cases, the different breeds used in the development process are well documented to prove the point.

One of the downsides of creating this range of 'pure breeds' is that maintaining them to the standard means that a high degree of inbreeding is required. It's common practice that stud cock birds are 'line-bred' using a father-to-daughter combination, and this goes on for generations. The inevitable result, though, is that the fertility rates of both the male and female birds gradually decrease. Nowadays it's common that many pure-bred hens will struggle to lay 80-90 eggs in a season, and infertility in male birds is a real problem. A classic example of this is the beautiful Buff Orpington, a pure-bred soft feather bird that's productive capacity has collapsed.

Every now and again breeders are forced to bring in a new line (fresh blood) to bolster productivity. In some cases the problems caused by in-breeding has led to such serious problems that the only option left is to cross-in another

Hybrid hens may not all be spectacular to look at, but they can make great and productive friends to have in the back garden

The Light Sussex was a fine utility fowl in its day, but now even a cracking example like this one would be eclipsed by a modern hybrid

type altogether in a bid to salvage the line. So the undeniable conclusion to all this is that, in fact, not many 'pure breeds' are actually pure at all!

Hybrid roots

So what is a hybrid? Well, in simple terms, it's the offspring from the cross-breeding of different chicken breeds. Hybrid chickens are made by crossing two other breeds possessing desirable characteristics, usually with a specific, business-orientated purpose in mind. So a cross may be made to enhance laying performance, vigour, breast size, weight gain, flesh colour, egg colour, egg size and colour sex-linkage etc.

I used to produce hundreds of Araucana chickens from which I selected my stock for showing. The Araucana cock bird carries the true, blue egg gene, particularly the black variety. My local commercial breeder used to buy my excess male birds, and used them in a breeding program to establish a hybrid, blue egg-laying hen that produced eggs in the right numbers, and of the desired colour to suit the demands of his supermarket customers. It's likely that he crossed a white egg-laying hybrid, based on the Leghorn, with my black Araucana males to avoid diluting the blue shell pigment.

The meat industry utilises hybrids with the large Indian Game in their ancestry, to maximise the size of the bird's breast. This, combined with heavy weight gain, are among the most desirable points the poultry industry seeks of its meat birds. As a result, these birds are ready for slaughter in just 12 weeks.

With all this in mind, it's clear that many in the Fancy who champion the virtues of popular and sought-after pure-breeds such as the Sussex, Rhode Island Red, Plymouth Rock and Jersey Giant, are misinformed as far as the purity of these breeds is concerned. To illustrate the point, let's consider the Rhode Island Red.

This breed was created in Adamsville, USA. One of the 'building blocks' used was the black-breasted red Malay cock, which had been imported from England. This infusion gave the

The Bluebelle is a very popular hybrid too; it's easy to see why!

breed its size, disease resistance, essentially docile nature and superior meat qualities. In 1925 the Rhode Island Red Club of America donated funds for an elegant monument to the bird in Adamsville (now on the National Register of Historic Places). But a competing monument to the breed was erected by the state in 1954, suggesting that it had been created not for the poultry fanciers, but for the many farmers who reared it commercially in the area. So, not much breed purity there then!

The Plymouth Rock, often called simply a 'Rock' or 'Barred Rock' (after the most popular colour), is another breed that originated in the United States. It was developed in New England during the early 1800s, by crossing Dominiques and Black Javas. The objective was to create a dual-purpose fowl, valued both for its meat and the hens' egg-laying ability. Much of the development work is believed to have been carried out by John C Bennett (1804-1867) and, as with the RIR, the development story rather destroys any idea about purity of breed.

Land of the Giants

There's a similar story behind the black Jersey Giant, created by John and Thomas Black during the late 1800s in Burlington County, New Jersey. The birds varied in colour to begin with, as most effort was focussed on developing a good size and confirmation, to ensure a good-sized roasting bird. Heavy breeds such as Black Java, Black Langshan and Dark Brahma were all mixed in to create the first examples.

Finally, the Sussex was created in the county of the same name more than a century ago, by crossing four separate breeds. The original plumage colours were brown, red, and speckled, but these were followed the light, buff and silver. The most recent variety – re-created after being lost – is the Coronation Sussex.

The breed was prized as a table fowl and, more recently, the Light Sussex proved a favourite and successful competitor in the laying trials of the 1930s. Today, the Sussex is a popular breed for both exhibitors and the backyard keeper. It's made a huge contribution to the poultry industry, and is one of

This is a Rhode Rock

the ancestors of the modern broiler. As such, it represents one of the oldest breeds that we have today but was, nevertheless, created by commercial breeders!

So there you have it, most birds are crossbreeds of one sort or

The Amber is a pretty little hybrid laying hen

another! Rather than bore you with the origin of the chicken species, those who turn their noses up at the thought of keeping hybrid birds are clearly missing an important point. The chicken breeds the Fanciers slavishly keep and dearly love were, in the most part, the hybrids of the 1920s and 1930s.

Fit for purpose?

The first question that any prospective poultry keeper should ask themselves is what are they intending to keep their birds for? If you can answer this question then the choice of the type of bird to keep is made simpler.

If your aim is to exhibit poultry – competing in the many PCGB-sponsored shows held all round the country – you'll need to buy the best pure-bred stock you can from a recognised and specialist breeder. These experts will have selectively bred their birds for the show bench, meaning that they'll offer the best possible starting point for the exhibition novice.

However, if your intentions are rather more practical, and egg laying performance is important to you, then it's worthwhile appreciating that the traditional pure-breeds are generally less robust, and don't offer the same laying potential as the modern hybrid utility breeds. I often make the comparison with mongrel and pedigree dogs; the pedigree breeds can be highly-strung and not terribly robust, while a good old mongrel will usually go on for years! Hybrid birds are typically rugged, easy to keep and they offer excellent laying potential. They're also very pretty birds for the back garden enthusiast, and can make great family pets thanks to their docile nature.

Of course, many of the pure breeds are exceedingly handsome too, but they can't generally deliver in the productivity stakes. If you're looking to keep birds for meat, the chances are you'd be doubly disappointed with a pure

bred, as many breeds are scrawny and thin compared to the much more affordable, quicker-maturing, speciality hybrid meat birds.

While some of the traditional dual-purpose breeds may have been thought satisfactory 70 years ago, few can argue that they compare favourably with today's modern hybrid alternative. Of course, there are certainly advantages in eating your own pure breed birds, in terms of the excellent flavour they offer and the peace of mind that comes from having reared them yourself and knowing that they are unadulterated. However, most families, if served up a roast Light Sussex chicken, would be horrified at the skinny offering placed in front of them.

Another misconception that I should correct is that hybrid birds are aggressive and spiteful. This simply isn't true. If they are housed well and treated with appropriate levels of husbandry so that their health and welfare is assured, then you won't have a problem. After all, if you subjected a Light Sussex to the sort of restrictive conditions found inside a battery unit, it too would become spiteful and cannibalistic.

There's no doubt in my mind that, given the right conditions and a common-sense approach, hybrid hens can represent every bit as attractive an option as their pure-bred alternatives. What's more, with purchase prices being lower, maintenance costs the same and egg production levels significantly higher, the arguments stack-up noticeably in their favour on practical grounds. So don't look down your nose at the hybrid hen – as a productive and enjoyable back garden bird it really is hard to beat.

House points

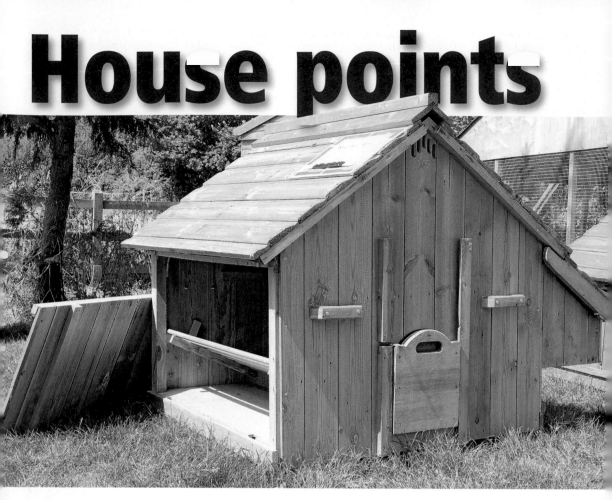

Chris Graham considers the most important practical features to look for when buying a poultry house

Above: A poultry house can be an attractive structure, but it must be functional and well-designed too. Large access panels that can be removed completely are a feature you'll come to really appreciate

With so much choice available these days, the apparently simple business of buying a poultry house has become surprisingly involved. The more you look, the more potential suppliers you find – but the real secret, as with buying birds themselves, is learning to tell good from bad.

As the poultry-keeping hobby has blossomed in recent times, so has the number people setting themselves up as hen house builders and suppliers. We're at the stage now where, at one extreme, you have large concerns importing mass-produced, flat-packed houses from China while, at the other, there's the one-man-in-his-shed operation building one-off units to his own design. Most of us occupy the territory in between these two ends of the economic scale, which is probably as it should be.

However, as with all other practical aspects of this fascinating hobby, there's a good deal to be considered when buying a hen house. Thankfully, despite the enormous variation in product quality we're presented with, it's perfectly possible to make the right decision if you follow a few commonsense purchase rules.

What shape?

Chicken fanciers truly are spoilt for choice when it comes to poultry house designs, there really is something to suit all tastes. Of course, with chickens being such attractive creatures, and backyard keepers wanting to maximise the visual impact of their poultry set-ups, it's easy to be drawn down a route that favours form over function. Never forget that a poultry house is there to provide a vital function, and there's a danger that those creations which place too much emphasis on cosmetic attractiveness can fall short in this respect.

While I'm not saying that it's

impossible to have an attractive poultry house I do think that buyers should always bear in mind that, first and foremost, a poultry house must provide its occupants with suitably-sized, draft-free, well-ventilated, dry and secure accommodation.

If you want to buy a purpose-made hen house then you basically have the choice between a simple, ark-style unit, a square-sided design with a flat, pent roof, or a square-sided style with a pitched, apex roof. There are variations on all three themes, and you can specify each with or without an integral run. Whether or not you opt for this depends on your situation, how much space you have available, how you'll be keeping the birds and your budget.

The ark-style houses – based on a simple, triangular structure – seem less popular with many keepers due to the headroom limitations inside. This can be especially true for those designs featuring a raised roosting compartment at one end. This is done to maximise run space but, with the living quarters squashed into the apex of the structure, roosting space can be dangerously restricted. Birds have been known to suffocate during hot weather under these conditions. But the ark-style houses remain attractive to the first-time buyer on a tight budget, because they tend to be the cheapest option.

The more conventional, straight-sided designs are costlier to buy, but are more popular among new and existing keepers nonetheless. In real terms they offer the best use of space, and their basic structure is such that designers find it easier to make them effectively weatherproof and readily accessible for simplified cleaning and bird management. The pent-roofed versions are cheaper than the pitched-roof alternatives but, for many people, they just don't look as attractive.

Happy roosting

If chickens aren't happy and content when shut inside the roosting compartment of their house then you're going to have serious problems. Apart from the key design requirements, which

Modern houses like this Haven, from Flyte So Fancy, *can feature a raised roosting compartment with a floor that's conveniently set at waist height to simplify cleaning operations*

POULTRY HOUSES: TEN TOP POINTS

The fact that a poultry house is the most expensive single item that the typical backyard hen-keeper has to buy makes it a very significant purchase indeed. But monetary value certainly isn't the only issue. At a practical level, the functionality of a hen house – and its day-to-day suitability to the birds that have to use it – may be considered more important considerations.

These factors combine to make hen house purchase an extremely important issue requiring plenty of thought and prior planning. Like the decision to start keeping poultry in the first place, the choice of house style should never be rushed, however tempting things may appear. Seeking out a good supplier – preferably a well-established manufacturer – can make all the difference. Straightforward, down-to-earth advice is essential as there are plenty of mistakes to be made.

The ten points covered here are among the most important aspects that anyone thinking about buying a hen house should consider. Mistakes can be costly, both in terms of wasted money and with regard to the ultimate welfare of the chickens you'll be housing.

1 The right house?

One of the fundamentals of poultry house choice is to match the unit design to the birds being kept. To do this effectively it's essential to understand the physical nature and the character of the birds you have, or are thinking of getting. Allowances need to be made for their height, weight, feathering, flightiness, aggressive tendencies etc. But, while this is relatively easy to do when dealing with a single breed, it can be a good deal more difficult to assess if you intend keeping a mixed flock. Many newcomers – often influenced by their children – opt to keep a couple of this breed, one of that, three of those. As a consequence, the result can be a hotchpotch of birds, with varying requirements, being housed together in a single unit that may suit some, but not others.

The hierarchy within a group of chickens, and the way in which individual birds interact, are key factors influencing harmonious living. Relations are easily upset by many things, including mixing different breeds, forcing birds to live in unsuitable surroundings or overcrowding them.

Houses that don't offer sufficient headroom, have poorly-positioned perches, badly-sited nest boxes or sub-standard construction leading to a draughty interior, are likely to cause problems for and with the occupants.

House/run combinations can be a practical option for beginners, assuming there is the space available to allow for the unit's regular movement on to fresh grass. Of course, these units aren't, in themselves, completely secure from fox attack, although fitting a wire mesh base can help. Interior space is obviously limited with these designs, so it's vital that no more than the recommended number of birds is kept.

The conventional, square-type house designs will offer more accommodation and can be more suitable for larger breeds. However, they'll need to be set within an adequately-sized run – or have one attached – so that the birds can be let out in safety; a more expensive option requiring more space.

2 Enough space?

This is a key issue and should always be one of the deciding factors in whether or not you keep poultry at all. Keeping hens in the back garden requires space. If you opt for a small, movable house/run combination standing on grass, then you must be prepared – and have the necessary room – to relocate it every two or three days. If you aren't able to do this, the birds will destroy the grass covering in no time at all, leaving just the bare earth.

Once this has happened, a common mistake is then to let the birds out to scratch around in the garden. Not only does this then expose the birds to potential predator attack, and allow them a free rein to demolish any flowers and vegetables they may find, but it also gives them a whole new sense of freedom which, in many instances, can be counterproductive.

Chickens are creatures of habit. They love routine and, by and large, don't miss what they haven't had. However, they certainly do notice when they are deprived of luxuries to which they've become accustomed. So confining them inside the run after a period of freedom can lead to increased levels of stress, greater susceptibility to disease, bullying and other behavioural problems. ➤

It's perfectly possible to keep five, medium sized hens (these are hybrid layers) in an 8x4' run like this, as long as the unit is moved on to fresh grass every two or three days

we'll cover later, keeping this area clean, dry and fresh is one of the essential requirements of a good husbandry program. While this will always be a chore to some degree, you can certainly make life a lot easier by buying a well-designed hen house in the first place.

The physical size of the house has a big influence on this. Given reasonable overall dimensions, designers are able to include large doors and other access points, which greatly simplify the cleaning-out process. Raising the house on legs – an important basic requirement anyway – will also help enormously in this respect, as it limits the amount of bending required. Some of today's smartest designs set the house floor at waist level, to make cleaning operations as easy as possible. This can be a real boon for elderly keepers, or those with mobility problems.

The amount of space available inside a roosting compartment is a crucial issue – over-crowding the birds must be avoided at all costs. This is an aspect that you'll have to check carefully, and be responsible for when buying. Remember that it's often in the seller's interest to maximise the bird capacity of a house, but this isn't always in the best interest of the birds. You, as the customer, need to be aware of the reality. Don't take for granted what the seller tells you; check for yourself.

The best rule of thumb is to work by perch length. Measure what's available inside the house

A detachable, external nest box can provide useful, additional access to the henhouse interior

and, allowing 8in/20cm of perch length for each bird, calculate how many the house could comfortably accommodate. For example, a house with a pair of 3ft/91.5cm perches should be suitable for eight large fowl chickens. Bantams, of course, don't require so much space, so work on 5in/13cm of perch per bird if you're planning to keep these.

Another good rule is always to

House and external nest box roof angles are important to ensure good water run-off. A good overhang between the main roof and the nest box is another great feature to look for; it'll help ensure the nest boxes stay dry inside

err on the side of under-capacity – in other words, buy a house that's slightly bigger than you need. Birds flourish with more rather than less space and the chances are that you'll end up buying more birds than you originally intended anyway! However, guard against going to the other extreme as well. Putting just three hens into a house designed for 24 won't work either. Although you may imagine the birds will revel in all that space, what'll actually happen is that they'll struggle to keep warm during cold weather, increasing their stress levels and making them more susceptible to disease.

An obvious way for the less scrupulous house builder to increase the bird capacity of a house, and thus its price, is to pack it full of perches! Watch for this, and make sure that any racking used has at least 8in/20cm between perches.

Ideally, perches should also be removable, which is a vital requirement in the fight against red mite. You can virtually guarantee red mite will colonise your hen house sooner or later, for it's almost impossible to banish this pest for good. Most keepers resign themselves to just minimising its effects by keeping the numbers in check. These tiny creatures don't live on the birds, but shelter inside the house during daylight hours, waiting to strike when the birds come in to roost at night. They hide away in nooks and crannies inside the house, and on the underside of perches; anywhere that affords them a bit of protection. Being able to remove perches will make it much easier to check and treat for red mite infestation on a regular basis.

Finally, on the subject of perches, their size and profile need to be considered too. Thin and spindly can be just as bad as thick and chunky. Most birds will be happiest and most comfortable roosting on a perch measuring about 2in/5cm square (slightly smaller for bantams), and that has its top two edges rounded-off.

The hole truth!
Every hen house needs a pop hole that's used by the birds to get in and out. The overall size of this can

So make sure that you buy a house that's suitably sized for the number of birds you intend to keep, and the amount of space you have available. Don't be tempted to buy more birds than you need. Remember that just three or four hybrid hens should provide more than enough fresh eggs for a hungry family.

3 Ventilation
This is an absolutely essential requirement for any poultry house. Adequate ventilation, without being draughty, is vital for the health and wellbeing of the birds living inside. Remember that a chicken's plumage acts like its own duvet; great in chillier conditions, but not so desirable during the hot, summer months. It's essential that all keepers offer their birds a shady, cool refuge, away from direct sunlight.

Plonking them in an unshaded run in the middle of a field will be their idea of hell. House/run combinations that provide shade can work well in this respect. The house itself needs to be well ventilated too. If you open the door of a poultry house and you're greeted with a blast of hot air, then it's far too hot and badly ventilated. Birds desperate to escape the sun will seek refuge inside a house, even if it's too hot, which can lead to untimely and unpleasant death.

Unfortunately, assessing whether ventilation levels are adequate is very difficult. Ideally, there should be vent gaps at the base of the roof, and at the ridge, so that the warm internal air is always being drawn out from the top.

Airflow though the house is vital in the winter too, contrary to what a lot of people think. It's quite common for inexperienced keepers to block up ventilation holes and gaps during cold spells, in the mistaken belief that it'll help their birds to stay warm. In fact, chickens are surprisingly tolerant of low temperatures, but what they can't deal with is static, damp air. This promotes the build-up of condensation and the onset of potentially very serious respiratory problems.

Poor airflow, combined with dirty bedding inside the house, will lead to the build-up of ammonia fumes, causing the birds real problems, as well as producing a potentially neighbour-upsetting smell.

4 Boxes and perches
Everyone knows that you need nest boxes inside a poultry house, but ➤

some get confused about how many. There's certainly no need for one per bird; happy hens will share. However opinions vary on the ideal allowance, with suggestions varying from three to seven birds per box.

One thing that everyone agrees on, though, is that nest boxes must be as dark as possible. Consequently, the well-thought-out house design will site them well away from the main entry point (pop hole). They also need to be deep enough to ensure a comfortable layer of bedding for the hen.

With regard to nest box bedding, avoid hay or straw, and opt for softwood shavings or one of the new hemp-based materials instead. Nest box 'barring' (in the form of some sort of shutter), can be a good idea too, to prevent birds from using the boxes as additional roosting space; it's important that they are kept clean, fresh and free from droppings.

Perches should be removable, and correctly positioned for the birds you intend to keep. If you fancy a large, tall breed, then make sure that headroom above the perches is sufficient, especially if you're considering a triangular, ark-style house design.

Heavy breeds will need perching that's not set too high off the floor, to avoid the risk of impact-related foot problems (bumblefoot). The width of the individual perches are important too, as is their shaping and spacing. Corners must be rounded-off for gripping comfort, and they should never be too narrow.

Many houses now feature perch racks, which are removable – essential for thorough cleaning and the fight against red mite.

5 Detail touches

It's often the little things than can make all the difference with a poultry house. Look for practical essentials such as sturdy lifting handles, long-lasting stainless steel screws and hinges, reliable and straightforward locking mechanisms on the doors, a smooth-running pop hole.

These are the sort of features that you can expect to find on professionally-made units but which can be lacking on the sort of product made by the many 'one man in his shed'-type operations now on the scene. They can also be missing on some of the cheap copies being imported from the Far East.

Sticking doors, stubborn pop holes, stiff hinges, loose or rusted ▶

Keeping it simple is always a good policy with poultry housing, as this Bedgebury night ark from Forsham illustrates. Note the generous access, removable perch rack and the use of plastic sheeting under the perches as an improvised 'droppings tray'

vary a lot from design to design, with bigger houses tending to have larger ones simply because there's more space to play with. So it's on smaller structures that you have to be more wary. In general terms, 13x13in/33x33cm is probably as big as you need to go, but watch for anything significantly smaller than this.

Ventilation is another absolutely key factor when considering a house purchase. It's very important that the roosting area remains well-ventilated at all times, but without being drafty. Ideally what you're after is a gentle but constant throughput of air, to avoid the build-up of moisture and/or fumes inside the house.

A well-designed house will achieve this with its main ventilation points positioned high on the walls, close to the roofline, and combined with smaller apertures and/or slots incorporated lower down, around doors and pop holes etc. Unfortunately, there's no accepted formula for easily calculating the ventilation requirements of any given house, or the size of the apertures needed

to provide it – you'll have to be guided by the supplier on this one. But it really is a vital issue, so ask lots of questions and be suspicious of anything that looks inadequate.

Two other important ventilation-related points include the fact that good airflow must be maintained throughout the year. Don't be tempted to block-up vents in the winter when the weather is colder. If your birds are healthy, well-cared

Where perching racks are used, ensure there's an eight-inch span between individual perches

A large access door is essential for day-to-day maintenance. Note the droppings board inside this house, and the sturdy legs raising the structure about five inches above the ground as an anti-rodent measure

for and in the right-sized house, then normally low temperatures shouldn't pose a problem. Also, give some thought to house orientation, with regard to prevailing winds etc. Don't position it so that rain and wind can easily drive straight in through either the pop hole or main vents.

Nest boxes can be mounted either internally or externally, with much depending on the size of the house. While an externally-mounted unit is generally regarded as preferable – offering less disruptive access – they do add considerably to the cost of a house, and need to be well designed if they're to remain dry inside. For these reasons, most smaller designs tend to have an internal unit

The two basic requirements for a good nest box are that it's sited at an appreciably lower level than the perches, and that it's as far away from the pop hole and perches as possible to help ensure that it's as quiet and dark as it can be. The relative height compared to the perches is important because it determines where the birds will roost. Chickens will naturally choose to roost at the highest available

point, so if the nest boxes happen to be positioned higher than the perches, then that's where the birds will settle for the night.

Timber choice

Wood thickness and treatment are both fundamental aspects in determining the working life of a hen house. Given the option, it's always better to opt for a house built from properly pressure-treated wood than one that's simply been painted with some sort of preservative. Pressure treatment offers a much more lasting effect than a traditionally-applied coating, and requires no maintenance during the first 10-20 years.

It's also very important that the wood is thoroughly dry before it's used to build a house. Damp wood will simply go mouldy and will also move as it dries out, opening up gaps and potentially letting in rain. Cut ends should be treated as well, to help prevent rotting and splitting as the wood ages. Check all these details with the supplier and, if anything sounds at all vague, then go elsewhere.

The thicker the timber used, the better. A heavy house is likely to be

fixings and handles that rot and snap off will become the bane of your poultry-keeping life!

6   Where to buy?

The poultry house sales sector is the largest of those which have sprung up to support the domestic keeper. Consequently, all sorts of operations have set themselves up in recent times offering houses and runs for sale; some are good, some are bad.

The more established operators, like Forshams, are suffering at the hands of 'copycat' builders from China, who delight in duplicating their designs, exporting them to the UK and undercutting the originals on price.

There are all manner of flat-pack alternatives available now too, plus plenty being made by one-man operations; spend just a few minutes on Google and you'll discover what a bewildering range of companies and products there currently is out there.

Our advice is to stick with a respected supplier which, preferably, builds its own units and can offer the sort of expert aftercare and practical advice that all new customers require. Remember that there's usually only one reason why something's cheap...

7   Cheap shed?

Garden shed conversions can represent great value for money, as long as you know exactly what you're doing. Many novices get suckered into the '£99 bargain' idea, but end up creating lots of problems for the birds due to inexperience and lack of knowledge.

Key problems are that garden sheds can be too light (big windows) and much too hot in the summer (no properly thought-out ventilation system). Also, they're not supplied with nest boxes, perches or pop holes, so you're going to have to add those yourself.

Unfortunately, there are plenty of people who look to the conversion of an existing structure as a money-saving option, be it a plastic Wendy house, an old caravan or a dog kennel. In practical terms, though, none of these is likely to perform as well as a custom-made poultry house and so generally represent a false economy.

8   Strong enough?

Another important factor that can be compromised on cheaper hen houses is the thickness of the wood used. You can assess this either by simply ➤

measuring it for yourself (look for ¾in/19mm as the ideal), or by flexing the larger panels to check for movement.

Large doors or roof sections that are made from wood that's too thin, or lacks adequate bracing, will be prone to twisting and warping with age. Inherent weakness like this will magnify as time passes, especially if the unit is regularly stressed during relocation.

Doors that twist will become ill-fitting, not only exposing the birds inside to a potential predator threat, but also letting in additional draughts.

9 Easy clean!

The best poultry house designs will include a good number of access points, primarily to aid regular cleaning of the interior. Large hinged or removable doors will make all the difference, particularly once the initial novelty of routine poultry housekeeping has worn off... which it certainly will!

The last thing you want to find yourself doing on a wet November morning is crawling and stretching to reach inside your poultry house, through a door that's badly located and too small. Think of these points when inspecting a house. Imagine what's going to be needed to clean it effectively, and assess how easy or difficult you feel that it will be.

Dropping trays and boards incorporated into the design can also be a useful, practical feature.

10 What to pay?

Finally, it's important not to skimp on your poultry house budget. Remember, it's the birds, not your wallet, that must be the priority. Seeking to buy the cheapest house you can find is the wrong approach. If you can't afford to get a well-made, professionally-built and thoughtfully-designed unit, then perhaps you should re-think your entry into the hobby altogether.

Overcrowding chickens is one of the most serious mistakes that any keeper can make, and it's one that's guaranteed to cause problems for the birds. Take advice from the house supplier about bird capacities, and be honest and accurate with them about which and how many chickens you intend keeping.

As a rough guide, use the perch length available in a house as a practical guide to capacity, allowing about 8in/20cm per bird.

a strong house but, as you would expect, those built from the best wood cost the most to buy. Doors and removable roof panels that feel flimsy and twist in use aren't a good sign if you're after longevity. So take a tape measure with you and check the width of the timber that's been used. If you're after the best quality then don't buy a house made from wood that's less than ¾in/19mm thick. A well-designed poultry house made from top quality, dry, treated timber will serve a caring keeper for 50 years. In contrast, something from the other end of the scale might only offer a couple of year's useful service before it becomes leaky and too distorted to function.

The final design aspect to consider is the roof. Essentially, there are three basic choices these days. Traditionally, many poultry houses had felt-covered roofs; a cheap and cheerful option. The downside is that this covering material has a relatively short life – it can be prone to bird and frost damage – and also provides a favourite refuge for red mite infestations. It's inexpensive to replace, of course, but many keepers are starting to regard having to do this an unnecessary nuisance.

Onduline is a modern alternative to roofing felt. It's a light-duty, tar-paper corrugated material supplied

in rigid panels that are simple to work with and easy to fix into place. It's been praised for it's anti-red-mite-attracting performance although, for some, its somewhat industrial appearance and the potential for condensation build-up count against it. The third option, and the most expensive one by far, is a timber roof – typically tongue and groove shiplap.

Finally, consider the angle of the roof. In general, larger house roofs should never be set at anything shallower than 40°, while the slope on smaller ones shouldn't be less than 32°. These two figures are the suggested minimums needed to guarantee effective water run-off, which is essential if the interior is to remain dry. Similar rules also apply to external nest box roofs, which should always be set at a minimum of 30°.

In the end, of course, hen house purchase is a very personal business. Your own preferences, plus the size of your budget, are likely to be among the most influential factors governing your choice. But, for the sake of your birds and their day-to-day maintenance needs, don't forget the practical aspects outlined above. Buying a hen house can cost a lot of money, so take the time to ensure that you spend your cash wisely on something that will do the job that's needed for a usefully long time. •

The simplicity of a well-designed interior – with perches and nest boxes removed – makes cleaning and pest control as easy as possible

Lighting the way

Bob Cross explains how lighting affects egg-laying performance and how careful control of day length can maximise production

We all tend to take light for granted, hardly giving it a second thought. But chickens are slightly different in so far as they rely on us to provide it for them and, as such, it's important that we get it right. However, unlike some other aspects of husbandry, the business of controlling the light your poultry receive isn't a precise one, and is frequently a cause of some confusion among keepers (especially those new to the hobby). But by following some basic principles, and with some careful manipulation, the results achieved can be very advantageous.

Most commercially-reared chickens are subjected to artificial lighting programs at some point in their lives. Meat birds produced intensively receive a 'long day' to encourage them to eat and, consequently, grow faster. But the light levels used are kept purposely low so that the birds remain as calm as possible, and losses through wasted energy are minimised.

Important times

Pullets being reared for laying do best if, after the first couple of weeks, they're given 'short days' of between eight and 10 hours. This will hold back the arrival of maturity until the bird is physically big enough to start laying, and then sustain egg production. Once again, though, the intensity may be reduced to control temperament. Laying and breeding stock graduate to longer days over a period of weeks at the end of the rearing phase, initially to stimulate and then to maintain production.

Domestic poultry keepers can make use of supplementary lighting too, and what follows will explain, in general terms, how to set about this.

Whatever program is devised, welfare legislation and codes of practice must be taken into account. The essence of this is that where natural light is insufficient to meet the birds physiological (normal functioning) and ethological (characteristic) needs, artificial lighting will be provided. In practical terms this means that very short days must be avoided; the minimum day length is usually accepted as being eight hours of continuous light.

All programmes should follow a 24-hour rhythm, and include an adequate, uninterrupted period of darkness that's equal to about one third of the day. So, in each 24-hour period, laying hens must receive about eight hours of darkness in which to rest.

When the lights go out there should also be some provision made for a period of twilight, to allow the birds to find their way to roost. This requires a dimming system that gradually reduces the light intensity before finally switching it off completely.

A minimum light level of five lux (basic unit of light intensity), but for preference not less than 10, is required inside a poultry house. A light meter is needed to gauge this but, as a guide, four lux is the point at which it becomes impossible to read newsprint.

So, to summarise, it's essential to follow a 24-hour cycle, of which at least eight hours are light and about eight are dark. There must also be a 'twilight zone' and very low light intensities should be avoided if possible. Even at extremes of the seasons in this country, natural lighting patterns tend to comply to these basic requirements. So, if in doubt don't interfere; leave the lighting to Mother Nature. However, for those keepers keen to use supplementary lighting to boost winter production, read on.

Assuming that the layers will be kept in a windowed house making use of natural light, this must be taken into account when devising your approach. As the natural light cannot be excluded, the

The light source in windowed houses is important; ideally some should come from above (note skylights fitted to this house)

TYPICAL SUNRISE/SUNSET THROUGHOUT THE YEAR

	Sunrise	Sunset
Jan 1	8.06am	4.02pm
Feb 1	7.39am	4.49pm
Mar 1	6.45am	5.41pm
Apr 1	6.35am	7.35pm
May 1	5.33am	8.24pm
Jun 1	4.48am	9.08pm
Jul 1	4.49am	9.21pm
Aug 1	5.25am	8.48pm
Sep 1	6.14am	7.46pm
Oct 1	7.01am	6.37pm
Nov 1	6.55am	4.33pm
Dec 1	7.44am	3.54pm

supplementary lighting program must 'ride on the back' of what's naturally provided. It's important to consider the following principles.

Avoiding mistakes
During the rearing phase, the light level must not be increased; it may be held at a constant level, or decreased. However, during the laying phase it must never be decreased, with the only options being to hold it constant, or increase it. It's also important that programs implemented during the rearing period are seen to continue through into the laying phase – in other words, when point-of-lay pullets are bought in they should receive as much, if not more, light than they did in the rearing house. Any program that complies with the above should work, but some may be more successful than others.

First, let's consider natural light. The graph on the next page, and the sunrise/sunset times given on this page, show how the day length is at its shortest in December – at about eight hours – and increases through the spring and summer to peak at around 17 hours in June (thick yellow line). Note that the weekly increase is not constant, week-on-week, but starts and finishes gradually with bigger weekly increments during the middle months. The same happens as the hours decrease from late

June through to December.

Increasing day lengths in the spring stimulate hens to lay, while the reduction in daylight hours during the autumn has the opposite effect. Providing additional light during the shorter days creates artificial spring- and summer-like conditions, keeping the birds in lay. However, it requires a little thought before the big switch-on takes place, and requirements will vary depending on the date at point-of-lay (POL). It's worth looking at a few examples.

Pullets housed at POL in March/April
(Lines C or D on graph)
The natural light is on the increase, so can be utilised fully using no supplementary supply. The birds will come into lay, and continue to do so over the longest day, after which the decreasing day length will hold them back a bit. To prevent this happening the day length must be maintained using additional, artificial lighting. Switching on and off can be done manually, but a time clock makes life an awful lot easier, and ensures it's not forgotten.

On the face of it, this may sound simple, only requiring about 20 minutes adding on every week to keep up with the reduction in the natural light. However, the fact that light is being lost at both ends of

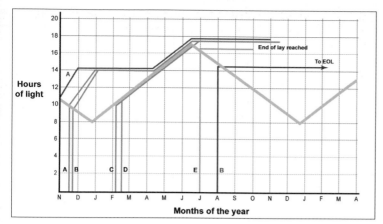

Line A (red): *Any birds housed POL at the end of October reared on 10 hours of light. This is increased to 14 hours, then held until the natural light takes over. It must be maintained at 17 hours after longest day (June).*

Line B (red): *Any birds housed POL. Day length is maintained until natural light takes over, and is then maintained as for line A (red).*

Line A (blue): *Hybrids housed in mid-November having received 10 hours during rearing. Light increased gradually to 14 hours over about six weeks, then held until natural light takes over, then maintained to end of lay after the longest day.*

Line B (blue): *Any birds POL, having being reared on a shorter day. Follow the same pattern as in Line A (blue).*

Lines C & D (blue): *Any birds housed POL mid-February through the spring. Whether reared on eight or 10 hours, they receive natural light until the longest day, after which it's maintained artificially.*

Line E (green): *Any birds housed mid-summer; maintain maximum day length with artificial light.*

the day must be taken into account, and the necessary allowance made. Probably the best solution is to add it all on in the morning, so the hens get up early, and go to roost at the natural dusk.

Pullets at POL during June/July
(Line E, on graph)
These birds will come into lay very fast – probably too fast – which, in itself, may prove problematic. The day length at housing must then be maintained henceforth in a similar manner to that already described.

Autumn- and winter-housed flocks
We now come to a situation where the day length may need increasing at some point. Light is usually increased by about an hour every seventh day, up to 15 or 16 hours a day (hybrids 14-15 hours). Sometimes the first two or three increments are doubled, especially where it coincides with the depths of winter.

Pullets housed as the days shorten should be treated as follows. If they are housed when the natural light is longer than that which they have received in the rearing house, this should be maintained with the use of artificial light as the days shorten (*Line B, on*

The accurate control of artificial light is a vital issue and, to avoid inadvertent mistakes, using a timer switch like this makes a lot of sense

graph). If less than 14 hours, it should be gradually increased up to this level and held there until the end of the laying season. However, less artificial light will be required as the days start to increase again, and dispensed with altogether when the days are the same as the artificially-extended one.

For naturally reared flocks, the day length at POL will be the same at housing. In this situation it's probably as well to let the hens begin laying before providing additional light. Then, once in lay, the day length can be boosted, but whatever is given must be held until the natural light catches up in the spring and takes over.

Pullets housed during December *(line A on graph)* must be started on the same day length as they received in the rearing shed. If this was eight hours a day, then natural light will suffice as this is on the increase from this point on anyway. Remember, though, that after June the natural hours start to decrease, so provision must be made from then on for a top-up.

Hybrid tips
Many of the laying hybrids sold at POL are reared on a slightly longer day (probably 10 hours), so this must be maintained until natural daylight levels catch up. This latter scenario is of interest because if these birds are housed in the winter months and only receive natural light, the result will be a decrease in day length. Should this happen, the birds will regress, the onset of lay will be delayed and those that have started are likely to stop temporarily. For this reason it's important to discover what day length bought-in pullets have been used to, so that this can be continued or progressed using artificial light. Once again, the minimum requirement is to maintain it until natural light catches up, then to make use of the increases.

At this point it is worth taking a breather to consider all of the above. On first reading it would appear complex, but subsequent analysis will reveal that all the options are variations on the basic theme, and any program so conceived should give satisfactory results.

All about runs

Above: Small, ark-style units like this are designed to be moved on a daily basis, but are all too easy to overcrowd with birds

How big, what shape, where, what fencing and what ground treatment? Chris Graham unravels the basic requirements for a good poultry run

One of the key messages that we regularly emphasise to anyone new to the poultry-keeping hobby is the importance of planning. It may sound boring and dull, but if you're serious about doing things right and ensuring that your birds enjoy life under the highest of welfare standards then rushing into the whole business on a wing and a prayer is the worst thing you can do.

Every aspect of what you're entering into requires careful thought. You must decide on the most suitable breed, the most appropriate type of housing, how you're going to look after them, who's going to do the work and when. Chickens are a commitment; they require regular and devoted care and attention, and that can turn out to be a struggle for those

leading busy 9-to-5 lifestyles. What's more, the birds' surroundings must be right if they're to flourish, both mentally and physically. Many newcomers fail to appreciate just how sensitive chickens are to stress, and what dramatic effects this can have on their general wellbeing.

One of the most common causes of stress among birds is overcrowding and, unfortunately, it's a common problem. New keepers, typically operating in limited space, can all too quickly fall into the trap of cramming too many birds into too small an area. Now, while this is usually done inadvertently, it's a hard fact we should all bear in mind. It becomes a particular concern when keepers start discovering the joys of home

This sort of wood frame-based run is easy to make and move. Convenient access is important and removable panels like the one shown, rather than smaller, hinged doors, are most practical

incubation. Stock numbers inevitably rocket, and lack of space very quickly becomes a serious issue.

While healthy hens will be perfectly happy kept shut up in a shed, this is only so if all their basic requirements are met – space, shelter, sun, fresh air, food, water, cleanliness etc. Plenty of backyard keepers skimp on house size, believing this to be a bit of a secondary issue, as their birds only have to roost inside. But don't forget that it's often very useful to be able to keep your birds inside for a few days at a time – if the weather is bad, for example – and in such circumstances you need to know that they will be perfectly happy and content in that environment.

Room to thrive

Many of you reading this may be surprised to learn that keeping just eight large fowl chickens under ideal conditions requires them to have a run area of at least 20x20m; a very large space if you pace it out, and probably bigger than the average suburban garden. Logic says that if you haven't got that amount of space available, then you keep correspondingly fewer birds, Unfortunately, though, logic often fails to make an appearance! Too many birds in an inadequate run represent an all too common welfare-related problem nowadays. So how much space have your chickens got? They can never have too much, but they can certainly have too little. That's Run Rule No.1!

Poultry runs are vital areas that the birds use for exercise, supplementing their diets and keeping occupied. At the most basic level they are incorporated into the hen house structure, creating a unit that's usually movable, but necessarily small. The next stage up from this is a free-standing run unit built from wood-framed, wire-meshed panels screwed or tied together. These can be butted up against the hen house, or used in isolation and whether or not a door is required is largely dependent on the size. Beyond this you're really looking at a fenced enclosure, which needs to be secure if you're serious about keeping foxes and other predators out.

Building an effective poultry enclosure needs planning and budgeting; unfortunately, it's not a cheap exercise.

One of the most basic requirements of any poultry run or enclosure is that it offers the birds some shade when they need it. This is a vital factor for their overall welfare and contentedness. With all breeds thought to have descended

Good run access is always an important aspect. Double gates like these mean that large structures can easily be moved in and out

solid, flat board roof will suffice. An added advantage of this approach is that it'll provide the ideal spot to create a dry dust bath (a necessity for helping birds deal with parasites). You can create this either using a natural depression in the earth, or with a large shallow box filled with dry, fine soil. The shelter will offer the birds a refuge from the heat of the summer sun, as well as something under which they can feel safe and secure. A chicken's worst nightmare is to be plonked down in the middle of an open field; they hate big skies. So never imagine that you're doing them a favour by locating the chicken run in a bright, airy part of your garden. If you have spare space available around trees and shrubs, then make use of that instead. The birds will thank you for it!

If you opt for the natural approach, evergreen bushes and trees (holly, for example) work well, as they offer maximum shade all year round. Fruit trees are good too, and the crops will inevitably benefit from the all the extra, natural fertiliser. But, at a practical level, try to avoid plants that are prickly or thorny. While this won't matter particularly to the birds, it'll certainly be a major factor for *you* when you're trying to catch them!

The available space will be the determining factor for a great many keepers but, if you do have a choice, then position the house so that it gets as much of the morning sun as possible. To ensure this set the front (or the side with the window, facing south-west.

If you can give your birds natural shade then so much the better. Evergreens, like this holly, are particularly handy. However, avoid poisonous plants like laburnum and ivy for obvious reasons

from Jungle Fowl, today's chickens feel at their happiest when free-ranging in a woodland-type environment. Overhead cover – preferably trees or large shrubs – is the ideal but, of course, not all keepers can provide such luxurious surroundings.

If there's no natural shade available in the area in which your birds are living, then you'll have to manufacture some – it's as simple as that. Even a basic structure with a

This sort of plastic windbreak material can be an effective way of providing temporary shade for birds in small runs

Allowing early sun into the house is certainly preferable to the much hotter afternoon sun.

Morning sun is also important for encouraging the birds to wake up and get going nice and early! In addition, try to orientate things so that the back wall of the house faces into the prevailing wind and rain. The last thing you want – or, more importantly, the birds want – is for driving rain and wind to be forcing its way in through the pop hole and around doors, whenever there's a storm.

There are also certain practical rules to be observed when placing the hen house within the run too. If it's a completely fox-proofed enclosure, and you're not that bothered about having to shut the birds in at night then you can, in theory, put the house anywhere you want inside the enclosure. But plonking it in the middle can be a nightmare if you decide you want to catch your birds during the day but hadn't shut them up the previous night; you'll end up chasing them round and round the house!

The one potential advantage of this approach is that, in cases where shade is lacking, the house itself can be raised sufficiently so that it doubles as a shelter too. Of course, hen houses should never stand directly on the ground anyway, to minimise the risk of rodent infestation underneath. But raising the structure more than the recommended 10-12in – so that the birds have sufficient headroom to walk about underneath – can work very well as long as it's secure (use railway sleepers or breeze blocks, plus 3x3in timber cross beams) and the hens can still get in and out of the house easily (avoid very steep entry ramps/ladders).

However, the more flexible approach – if you have the space – is to position the house outside the run, so that it forms a part of one of the sides. The front of the house (the side with the pop hole in it) should obviously face into run, with the perimeter fencing extending away on either side from the corners of the house. The advantages of this are that it maximises the run area – the house isn't taking up valuable space inside – and it simplifies access to the

Having the space firstly to avoid overcrowding and, secondly, to enable run areas to be 'rested' while grass recovers/grows, are genuine benefits for any poultry keeper.

house and nest boxes because there's no need to risk disrupting the hens by entering the run at all when cleaning the house or collecting eggs. It also makes shutting the birds in simpler as they have nothing to run behind.

Floor coverings

There are few creatures as adept at clearing vegetation as the chicken. They love nothing better than scratching and pecking at fresh, young grass shoots, and digging for insects. The problem this creates for the keeper is that they'll quickly destroy virtually any vegetation they are given access to. I've seen compounds of three-foot high nettles demolished quicker than you'd ever imagine by just a handful of active hens!

The upshot of this behaviour is that a luxuriant lawn will be converted into a muddy mess in a matter of days, which is why runs need to be either very large, or small enough to move around on a daily basis.

Grass is always going to struggle against a chicken onslaught, unless you have the space to be methodical about a 'grazing' plan. Those with enough room to sub-divide the run area into workably sized pockets should be able to keep the grass going by 'resting' sections as they need it. For the rest of us, though, the

likelihood is that we'll be fighting a losing battle.

Re-seeding (sewn thickly) will be required on a regular basis, and the young grass must be given time to establish itself if it's to stand any chance. You'll get the best performance by sowing a ryegrass/clover mix, but even this won't survive the close confinement of birds. Don't buy seed from the

Re-seeding will be a regular job for anyone keeping chickens on grass. A 'patching mix' offers an affordable and durable combination of ryegrasses

local garden centre, go to a specialist, independent supplier instead for a better deal. Also, look out for an agricultural option called 'patching mix', which is what farmers use for re-seeding worn areas in fields; it's a mixture of ryegrass types and offers a very affordable option. Lime should be applied (hand-sprinkled) in the spring as an effective measure against coccidiosis – it will dry-out and kill the oocyst. It will also help to maintain the right pH in the soil (6.5-7.0 is necessary for grass to thrive).

Over-stocked runs, apart from causing all sorts of welfare-related problems with the birds, can also turn the ground 'sour'. This happens most commonly if too many birds are kept in a confined run with an earth floor, and then neglected. Remember that the smaller the run area, the greater will be the level of attention needed by the birds to keep them fit and healthy. Droppings that are allowed to build up and get trodden into a bare earth surface will pollute the soil, raising its acidity and making it 'sour'.

The best way to deal with this is to dig over the soil to a depth of about 25cm, treating it with a lime dressing as you do so, to freshen it up. Ideally it'll then be given time to recover and, best of all, re-seeded with grass. But this isn't always possible, especially when space it at a premium. In those circumstances, it really is better to create a more 'inert' surface that will be easier to manage. Gravel, shingle or wood chips can all work well. You could even run your birds on a solid concrete floor, or a raised, wire mesh surface. While these last two may sound somewhat utilitarian, they can both be extremely effective and easy to manage.

Any form of leaf litter, wood chips etc must at least 6in deep to be effective. Bracken can be very good if mixed in, as it's a natural insect deterrent. Wet, damp runs create unpleasant smells, and increase the risk of dirty eggs and potential salmonella or eColi infections. If the chicken muck and manure builds up in the summer, it offers perfect fly breeding conditions, which can create problems with neighbours.

Although grass is the ideal surface on which to keep hens, it's not always possible when space is tight. A shingle covering like this, although appearing utilitarian, can work very well

As far as overall run shape is concerned, it seems that the one to avoid is a square. Studies into livestock behaviour have established this to be the worst and most unsettling shape for any sort of stock enclosure, including poultry runs. Animals and birds evidently feel more relaxed in a rectangular-shaped area than a square one.

Fencing options

The generally accepted ideal height for a chicken run fence is two metres, and this is what you should aim for if circumstances and budgets allow. Situations vary enormously though, and so many owners will be forced to compromise on this for all sorts of practical reasons. However, the general principles remain the same

Wire mesh clipped to a strainer wire. The special pliers and clips needed to do this are available from fencing specialists, together with all the other raw materials required

Creating a wire mesh overhang like this will help prevent 'climbers' like mink gaining access.

in terms of build quality and security, so use the following suggestions for the ideal set-up as a reference, picking out the aspects which are most relevant to your own situation.

The best approach to creating a two-metre high enclosure fence is to use two separate runs of wire mesh, rather than a single one; it's much easier to manage. The two

'strips' should be supported on straining wires strung between the posts. Post size and spacing are both important factors, if the fence is to remain tight, effective and durable. The rule of thumb is that the posts are spaced at 3m intervals. You must also place a strainer post at each corner, which is slightly thicker, and secured more firmly, than those down the sides. Use 10x10cm or, at a push, 7.5x7.5cm tanalised timber for the strainer posts, and 5x5cm for the regular posts (deer fence posts are ideal).

The strainer posts will also need to be strutted with angled, solid timber braces for additional strength and support. Also, if you're building very long runs of straight enclosure fence, then you'll need to add in additional strainer posts every 60m or so. Strainer posts are set in concrete to a depth of three feet. The rest are sunk only two feet into the earth using a post hammer – concrete isn't necessary for the ordinary posts.

With the posts in place, dig a narrow trench all around the outside at the base of the posts, into which you'll sink the fencing wire to a depth of about 45cm, as an anti-digging measure. Use sturdy wire for the strainer, and fix three runs to the posts – one at ground

level, the second about half way up and the third close to the top of the posts. You'll need to set the positioning of these wires carefully, to allow for the buried depth of mesh at the base. These wires are then tightened using wire tensioners (available from fencing specialists). Attach the lower run of wire mesh first, all the way around the enclosure, clipping it at regular intervals to the lower two strainer wires. Repeat the process with the second run of mesh, attaching it to the middle strainer wire first, then hinging it up and clipping it securely to the top strainer. Then, if the posts ever move in the future, all you need to do is take up the slack with the wire tensioners to return the fence to its original tightness.

Of course, the fence is only going to be as good as the material you build it with. If you use poor quality timber and inadequate wire then it's just not going to do the required job. Ideally, 2m-high perimeter fences built to surround a large compound should incorporate two types of wire to provide a high-security barrier against predators. Both layers of wire are mounted on the outside of the posts, for added security. A high-tensile deer fence provides the strength while a much finer, rabbit-type wire mesh provides a second security layer. Although the square-meshed deer fencing is certainly strong, and will keep your chickens inside the run, the gaps in its mesh are big enough to allow a determined fox through; and other indiscriminate killers such as the mink. This is why doubling-up with the rabbit mesh is so important. Either layer, on its own, couldn't be relied upon to provide the security needed.

Shock tactics

If foxes are a serious problem where you live, then you really must be prepared to install some electric defences around your poultry enclosure. This may sound a bit draconian, but it really is necessary if you're serious about keeping the predators out. Talk to anyone who's experienced the shock and horror of a bad fox attack – which can wipe out an entire flock – and you'll discover

Not only is this poultry enclosure gate secured with weldmesh, there's also an electrified wire running across in front of it, and a buried log below to help prevent digging access

Sturdy, well-tensioned fencing featuring a predator-repelling combination of deer and rabbit wire meshes plus electricity

the fence and the other at the top; both, obviously, on the outside. The lower one should be set at about nine inches above the ground; just about nose-height for a fox! Its distance from the fence is important too. Set it too far away (any more than about nine inches), and the fox will jump over into the gap on the other side, and then start climbing the fence or digging down under it. You can either mount this electrified wire on a series of posts knocked into the ground, or buy short metal arms, with insulators on the end, which can be mounted conveniently on the fence posts.

The trouble is that, despite this level of protection, it's still almost impossible to keep every potential predator out of your poultry run. By setting the electric wires at the distances described, you leave yourself open to attacks from formidable foes such as the mink. These, although more scarce than foxes, will happily pass under the electric wires and dig under or climb the fence. Just about the only practical thing you can do to deter the 'climbers' is to create a wire overhang near the top of the fence.

Get shorty!

It's important to keep vegetation levels down around your run fence, especially if you're using an electric rodent deterrent system. There's no more effective way of causing an electrical short – and, thus, the disabling of the whole system – than allowing grass and weeds to grow up around an electrified wire.

The method you use for keeping this growth in check largely depends on how much effort you want to put in. One of the simplest solutions is to use a specialist weed-killing product, such as Glycosate. If you chose this option – those who prefer to avoid the use of toxic chemicals may not – take care to keep the spray off the wire as it can promote corrosion. Alternatively you can use a strimmer regularly along the base of the fence or, perhaps most environmentally-friendly of all, run a layer of weed suppressant material (heavy plastic sheeting, or damp proof coarse material works well) that's pegged securely into place at regular intervals.

that it's not something they want to go through twice. Things can be doubly bad if your birds are family pets, and you have to try to explain what's happened to young children.

You can buy electrified plastic mesh-type fencing, but this is really only intended to enclose birds on a temporary basis, when their free-ranging activities are being restricted, for example. However, if you're thinking about electrifying a permanent run fence, then you'll have to install a wire-based system that's either battery or mains-powered. The choice between the two comes down to personal preference and budget.

While most experienced breeders opt for a mains-based system, the car battery-powered alternatives do offer a greater degree of operational flexibility – you can literally use them wherever you want. On the downside, though, batteries do go flat and, as is the way with these things, this usually happens at the most inopportune moment! One option to help avoid this is to install a solar-powered charging system, but

this can be expensive. Foxes have a uncanny ability of knowing when the current is weak, and breaking through!

The mains-powered set-up sends current in a single circuit that runs along two wires, one at the base of

Electrified fences mustn't be allowed to become overgrown. Short circuits caused by touching branches or vegetation can prove disastrous

Feeding frenzy

A modern poultry ration is more than simple 'chicken feed' – Bob Cross does a practical assessment of how best to treat your birds with regards to food and dietary supplements

'Chicken feed' is an expression often used to describe something of trivial value, no doubt derived from the fact that in the dim and distant past, chickens were fed on corn consisting of the smaller, cheaper grains.

This is no longer the case, of course. Modern poultry feeds are compounded from the highest quality ingredients to ensure that the birds eating them enjoy a diet that's been formulated to the nth degree. The monetary value of these rations represents possibly the biggest single input into production costs.

Feeding poultry is a relatively simple aspect of husbandry, but confusion may arise as a result of the range of feeds available, and the variety of equipment on the market used to put it in front of the birds. The following notes have been put together help explain, in general terms, how poultry may be fed.

What food?

All poultry must be fed a complete and wholesome diet, and it's vital that the feed is presented to them in a clean and fresh state.

The simplest way is to buy a proprietary brand designed for the purpose; layers feed for laying stock, grower formulation for growers, turkey for turkeys etc. These will contain everything the bird needs for health and performance.

Chick Starter is fed for the first 6-8 weeks, after which the birds need to be moved on to a grower ration. Continue with this up until about two weeks before the first eggs are expected, at which point they should be switched to a layers ration. The timings are not critical and, while it's advisable to feed the starter diet for at least the first six weeks, little harm will come from feeding it beyond eight weeks, especially if you are trying to meet body weight targets.

However, it's important to have got the birds off the growers diet before the onset of laying, to make sure that drug residues are not carried over into the eggs. Layer diets are fairly standard in formulation, and this

Young birds must be fed on chick crumb for the first 6-8 weeks, after which theycan be moved on to a growers ration

'one size fits all' aspect works reasonably well for the domestic keeper. There may be a case (such as when feeding birds with large appetites) for feeding one of the lower-protein layer diets that are available, thus saving a few pence on this aspect of the food that would have been wasted anyway.

Starter and grower diets may contain a drug to help prevent coccidiosis, and this is a useful supplement. This sort of treated

feed should be used until the 'teenage' weeks are reached, by which time the bird should have developed an effective natural resistance to the disease. While it doesn't guarantee freedom from coccidiosis, feeding this type of ration certainly helps and, if the birds do succumb, the onset may be slower, giving time to seek help before too much damage is done.

For breeding stock – especially those kept in confinement – it's worth using a breeder ration. This will be similar to a laying diet, but with a fortified vitamin and mineral content. If breeder feed is not readily available, then extra vitamins can be given in the drinking water or, more naturally, by offering fresh green food such as cabbages etc.

Crumbs, pellets, mash or meal?

Day-old chicks are usually started on crumbs simply because the fine milling used in the manufacture of this feed type means that the tiny pieces are easily eaten by even the smallest of chicks. Grower and layer diets are available in either pelleted or meal form. The former – being almost foolproof – has much to recommend it. The danger with feeding birds dry meal is that they tend to actively pick out the bits they like best and, in so doing,

One glance at a modern poultry feed label leaves you in no doubt about the thought and ingredient range that goes into these high-specification products

Matching the right type and size of feed to the age of your birds is an important requirement for any poultry keeper hoping for the best from his or her birds

that where dry meal is fed the drinkers will need to be cleaned on a daily basis. Food matter that inevitably finds its way into the water and settles to the bottom will quickly ferment. Water can be added to dry meal to make a 'wet' mash, details of which follow later.

One very important thing to avoid is feeding a grain-only diet. Despite all the idyllic images on television and in books, doing this is likely to lead to disappointment. The problem is that cereals, in general, only contain about 10% protein, and not only is this well below the bird's requirements in terms of quantity, but the quality is inadequate as well. The same applies to feeding a bread-based diet – bread, of course, is essentially being a grain-based product. However, grain can be used to dilute rations where feed intake is high and, as a guide, up to 20% of the daily allowance can be given like this.

Wheat is the most popular option, being readily available and palatable. Oats are useful too, although not relished by the birds to the same extent. The other option is kibbled maize, which is not only enjoyed by the birds, but will also add to the yolk colour – especially if the laying flock is living inside.

unintentionally fall short from a nutritional needs point of view. Furthermore, as they feed, there's also a tendency for individual food particles to get flicked out of the feeder, and be wasted.

Another consequence of feeding meal is that it usually takes longer to eat because, being rather

unpalatable, the birds need to keep stopping for a drink. But a positive aspect of this is that the extra activity can be helpful in keeping the birds occupied; particularly beneficial where there are competition or vice issues within the flock.

It's also worth noting, however,

Gritty business

Insoluble grit must be made available to your birds at all times (whatever the breed). Soluble grit can be given to laying hens, but never to growing stock.

These two types of grit are available as a mixture, or can be bought separately. The insoluble type includes flint and granite, and is very important to the bird for aiding the digestion of its food – it almost acts as the hen's teeth! This grit is graded into different sizes for varying applications (suitable for chicks, growers, layers and turkeys etc).

Once swallowed by the bird, the particles of grit enter – and are then held in – the gizzard, where they're then used to grind the food up so that it can be more easily digested as it continues its journey on through the bird. It's worth noting that grit that's too small will simply pass straight through and,

Grit is an important dietary requirement, and there are both insoluble and soluble types. This is oyster shell (soluble grit) given to aid bone development and eggshell quality. However, this should not be fed to growing stock; only to layers

If your birds aren't able to free-range, then a purpose-made grit box like this is a good idea

therefore, will be ineffective as a digestive aid. Consequently, it's best to move on to the next size (as the bird develops) sooner rather than later.

Grit should be provided, regularly though not constantly, in separate containers. But it can also be added to the food and, as a guide, a couple of handfuls every fortnight should suffice. As most feeds are provided in a ground-up form, insoluble grit would not appear an essential requirement of the diet. However, it is worth inclusion as it will aid digestion and help get a little extra out of the feed, and an important reason for using it is to prevent digestive blockages should the bird pick up fibrous materials such as long grass, straw etc.

Soluble forms of grit include limestone, and those containing either oyster or cockle shells. These are dissolved during digestion and the calcium contained in them is used by the bird for either bone development or eggshell production. Laying rations will contain enough calcium even for hens with small food intakes and at peak of lay. In theory, there's no need to supplement, but offering a bit of oyster shell may be useful towards the end of lay, and at any other time that shell problems occur. Growing stock, however, will have no need for additional soluble grit and, indeed, it may actually be detrimental to give it.

Soluble or mixed grits should be offered to adult stock in a similar manner to insoluble kinds.

How much food?

It's not possible to put a precise figure on chicken food consumption rates. Factors such as a bird's size, health status, rate of lay and the environment in which it's kept are just a few of the contributory aspects that have a bearing on how much a bird eats. As a rough guide, though, refer to the following table:

HOW MUCH FOOD?

Type of bird	Feed consumption per day
Day-old chick (bantam)	3g
Day-old chick (large fowl)	5g
Bantam (adult)	50-70g
Laying hybrid	120-140g
Meat hybrid (six weeks old)	145g
Traditional breed (adult)	160-200g

As mentioned already, most poultry feeds are fed in a dry state, in either crumb, mash/meal or pellet form. Feed is also usually made available so that it's in front of the birds at all times. In most instances this works well, and the birds eat according to their needs. But where this system isn't

It's hard to be specific about feed quantities because it's impossible to ensure that each bird eats the same

WHICH GRIT, WHEN?

Grit size	Age
Chick	2 days-3 weeks
Grower	3 weeks-10 weeks
Layer	10 weeks onwards

adopted, feed must be provided on a daily basis to comply with welfare requirements.

Day-old chicks reared naturally are shown how, what and where to eat by the broody hen. Youngsters reared artificially, using an incubator, don't get such a practical helping hand, of course, so the feed must always be placed so that it's simplicity itself for them to find. It's often a good idea for the first few days to sprinkle the chick crumb on sheets of paper or card, as well as in the feeders, to ensure every chick finds its fair share. Getting them eating and drinking at the earliest opportunity is very important, and must always be a priority.

Although this sprinkling approach may well lead to some wastage of food, doing it carefully can keep this to a perfectly manageable minimum. Also, the slight savings you'd make by *not* doing this would almost certainly be outweighed by the death of even one chick through starvation.

The feeding pattern of chicks reared with a broody hen is different form those reared under a heat lamp. The former will not eat during the night and, overall, their intake will be less than those eating 24 hours a day. This will be reflected in the body size initially, but any difference should have evened itself out as the rearing period draws to a close, all else being equal.

This rearing stage is an obviously crucial one and, in most cases, a bird's natural appetite should be enough to see it through these first few weeks without a problem. With some of the big, heavy breeds that have large appetites, though, the reverse may be more applicable, with some degree of feed restriction being appropriate. What you're always after is a body condition that's 'fit' and not 'fat'. This, of course, is as true for chickens during the early stages as it is for the rest of their lives. •

Feeders and drinkers

There's a wealth of choice when it comes to equipment that delivers food and drink to your chooks – Bob Cross looks at the pros and cons of various types

One of the main factors influencing food consumption (and overall costs) is wastage, be it caused by spillage or the birds flicking food out of the trough as they eat.

Once this sort of feed gets on to the floor, it's unlikely to be eaten if supplies are still available in the feeder. Although chickens tend to waste more mash when it's fed dry, the biggest single cause of losses is typically the feeder itself – either being a poor design, or badly set up.

Which feeder?

Essentially, poultry feeders can be divided into three basic types; trough, hopper or tube. The first of these represents the simplest option, and there is a range of design alternatives available, but troughs are perhaps the least suited of the three for outdoor use.

Big feeding units like this should never be regarded as a convenient solution to long-term feeding. All birds need daily care and observation

A straightforward trough offers one of the simplest feeding solutions. A rolled top edge like this is a good idea. Troughs need to be raised off the ground at a convenient height for the birds using them.

As with feed troughs, the base tray height should be set at the birds' back or shoulder height. If the gap is adjustable, it should be set at about 1cm to ensure a good flow of pellets. Mash (and chick crumb) can have a tendency to 'bridge' in the feeder, halting supply. For this reason, a slightly larger gap should be set with these feeds. However, avoid having too much food in the base of the feeder as this will lead to wastage.

Hoppers are a variation on the tube feeder theme, with the only real differences being that they are free-standing (on legs) and have a canopy, making them suitable for use outside.

However, in the right situation, they can represent a very practical feeding solution, although there are a few important considerations to bear in mind.

For a start, it's important that they are deep enough to hold enough for one day's feeding, and that this amount of food should only come one third of the way up the sides. Filling a trough any higher than this will simply cause too much wastage, as the birds will flick it out on to the floor as they eat. However, the trough should not be so deep that the bird cannot comfortably reach in to access the food. Different sizes are available and it's obviously important that appropriate ones are used with regard to the age/size of the birds being fed. Troughs aren't the most suitable way of offering food on a constant basis. Wastage can be minimised by using troughs designed with an inward-facing, rolled lip running around the top edge.

A further waste-reducing refinement worth considering is a trough cover. This may be a 'toast rack'-type arrangement, which prevents the birds from flicking their heads as they eat or, in the case of chick feeders, a full cover with pre-cut feeding holes. A third alternative is a spinning rail along each top edge, which will prevent perching on the sides and thus reduce contamination of the food below. Whichever you choose, though, it's important to make sure that all the birds have easy access

to the food, and are not excluded due to large combs etc.

Most feed troughs are designed to sit directly on the ground, but some form of height adjustment is usually sensible to prevent them filling with floor litter. They can be set on blocks or trestles, or suspended and raised as the birds grow. As a rule of thumb, the height of a trough's lip should match that of the bird's back or shoulder using it.

Tube feeders

These are made from either plastic or galvanised steel, and consist of a cylindrical feed storage tube fixed to a circular base tray; a small gap between the two allows the feed to flow from the cylinder into the tray. This important gap can be adjustable, or is pre-set during manufacture. The gravity-feed system delivers a small amount of food, which is then automatically replenished as it's consumed.

The choice between plastic or metal construction is largely a personal one. Both should work perfectly well, although the latter are more expensive. Better designs will feature short, radial spars that extend out from the base of the cylinder, across the 'trough' in the tray base, as an anti-waste measure to help prevent food being flicked out.

Typically tube feeders will be suspended from the hen house roof, at a height that's appropriate to the age of the birds being fed.

Note the radial vanes at the base of this plastic feeder, which are designed to minimise wastage by reducing the amount of feed that gets flicked out as the chickens eat

Feed storage

All feed types have a limited shelf life. Whole grains, if stored correctly, can be kept for quite some time, but the ground, pelleted or crumb forms don't keep for nearly as long – usually about six weeks after manufacture.

All feed should be consumed ahead of the 'best before' date for the best results. Leaving it longer than this can see a deterioration of the vitamin content, oxidation of the fats and oils plus the formation of mould.

To optimise feed condition it should be stored in a dry, cool place, out of direct sunlight. It should always be bought in sensible amounts, bearing in mind the sell-by date aspect, and must be kept in vermin-proof containers. The more airtight, the better.

Breeding stock – and especially birds kept in confinement – rely on the vitamins in the feed for their wellbeing, so storage is a key issue. Feeding mouldy food will harm your birds, as these growths produce mycotoxins, which can lead to poor general performance and even death.

Mould can sometimes be seen; it'll often turn the feed white or a bluey-green. But even before the visible signs, you should be able to notice an obvious smell. Similarly, if you discover moths lurking in feed bags or bins, it's a sign that the food is stale. Needless to say, neither stale nor mouldy food should be used.

Water, water

Welfare regulations require that poultry have access to clean, fresh water at all times and, as it costs virtually nothing, there's no point in restricting it.

It's a vital requirement for life; an animal can lose all of its fat and half of its protein (muscle) and survive to rebuild its reserves. But if it loses just one tenth of its body moisture, it dies. Water shortages will hinder both growth and egg production. If deprivation continues, laying will cease and the bird will go into a moult. Dehydration will follow, signalled by lethargy/weakness, shrivelled combs, sunken faces, after which comes death.

So the constant supply of fresh water represents a crucial health and welfare requirement, but the way in which it's presented to the birds is important too, with the type of drinker used playing a key role.

Open troughs or bowls are unsatisfactory for chickens – the birds tend to walk in them and they quickly become contaminated. They may be suitable for waterfowl as these birds need to submerge their heads, but even so they should not allow them bodily access. Founts are the most suitable way of

You can buy metal or plastic drinkers, with the latter normally being the more affordable option. A constant supply of fresh, clean drinking water is vital to the health and wellbeing of all poultry

Plastic drinkers have the advantage of clearly showing the level of water remaining. Ideally, they shouldn't be placed directly on the ground like this since it's harder for the birds to use and also leads to disease and parasite-promoting damp patches on the ground

watering chickens. Made of plastic or galvanised steel, they are available with capacities ranging from one to 20 litres.

The size used should be large enough to store a generous day's consumption for the birds using it. A drinker should never be regarded as a reservoir for a week's supply.

Plastic drinkers have much to recommend them – they're much cheaper than metal ones, probably more durable and the level of water can be visually checked. On the downside, they do go green with algae if used outside, and some become brittle after prolonged exposure to sunlight.

The metal drinker's main failings include cost and a tendency to become smelly and slimy inside. However, on the plus side, they're more stable, so less likely to blow away or get knocked over as they empty.

Watering can be semi-automated by using 'bell' drinkers – a plastic, bell-shaped drinker with integral flow control valve, suspended on an adjustable cord and fed by a low-pressure supply from a header tank. The water flow is governed by weight, being opened as water from the drinking channel around the base of the bell is consumed.

While these units can certainly reduce labour, they're not without their problems. The fact that they're suspended means that knocking them sets them swinging like a pendulum, creating spillages below. They can't be regarded as fully automatic, and need checking on a daily basis. Also, regular cleaning is essential, especially when being used in dusty buildings – neglect can transform the water into a bacterial broth!

Commercially, most chickens are watered using nipple-drinker systems and, while these could be adapted for small flock situations, it would be difficult to justify.

Easy access

Drinkers – there should be more than one – should be sited and set to give birds easy access. Place

Semi-automatic bell drinker systems certainly save work and time, but they're not the complete answer as daily checks are still essential

them out of direct sunlight, across the ranging area and move them as the surrounding area becomes worn. With newly-housed birds (and with flocks where some are

reluctant to venture outside) water must be provided inside as well as out.

Drinking fonts require little by way of setting, but they should be positioned at a height that makes drinking easy (similar to feeder height). It's not good to stand them directly on the ground anyway, not only because they are more easily contaminated, but because stooping low to use them means that a lot of water drains from the bird's beak before it gets a chance to tip its head back. Spilt water leads to wet patches, providing an ideal breeding ground for pathogenic bacteria, parasitic worms and the organisms responsible for diseases like coccidiosis.

The depth of water is fixed by the design of fount drinkers, but is adjustable with bell drinkers. Typically, you need no more than 1cm of depth. Special chick founts are available with narrow, shallow water rings. Standard units can be adapted by partially filling with washed pebbles, or a piece of hose pipe. •

Handy business

Terry Beebe offers an introduction to a vital skill that all poultry keepers should master – catching and handling birds

I'm often asked why it's so important to handle poultry, and always take time to emphasise to people just what a vital factor regular handling really is. Unfortunately, plenty of keepers ignore this aspect, failing to appreciate the many benefits to be gained from a more hands-on approach with their birds.

Handling poultry should form a part of every poultry enthusiasts' good husbandry program. It offers keepers the ideal opportunity to assess their birds for a whole range of potentially very important problems including parasitic infestation, feather loss, injury and overall health. It also provides the chance to make detailed inspections of other likely troublespots, including the bird's eyes, legs and vent area. It's difficult to reliably monitor any of these key factors from a distance, simply by watching your birds as they move around in their run or on range.

Another advantage of regular handling is that it gives the opportunity to conveniently dust the birds against lice and mites.

Many benefits

But it's not all about straightforward practical benefits, although these are obviously extremely important. The regular handling of poultry should be a pleasurable experience for the keeper too. It'll get you more involved with your birds, and will definitely enhance the relationship you have with your stock. Birds that are handled regularly from a young age will mature into more friendly, docile and manageable creatures than those that aren't. This has obvious advantages from an everyday, practical point of view, especially if you have children in the family and/or a small garden.

Getting birds used to being handled (and thereby accustomed to being around humans) also makes life much simpler with regard to general keeping. You'll find them relaxed in your presence and much easier to deal with accordingly. Checking the nest boxes, or catching them up in the evening should you need to put them to bed early, will become routinely easy. What you've got to remember is that chickens are more intelligent than many people give them credit for. They are creatures of habit too, and love routine, quickly learning to act in a way that suits both themselves and their keeper.

Good handling

However, all this presupposes that you set about your handling in the correct way. Doing it wrong can do

Definitely not the way to do it. Birds should never be held by their legs, wings or feet – it's cruel, painful and can cause serious injury

Never grab for a wing like this when catching a bird; damage can be all too easy to inflict

more harm than good, upsetting the birds and undoing any work you may have done beforehand on developing their tameness. Chickens are easily spooked, and the sight of a lumbering human crashing around inside their run, making wild lunges in an attempt to catch them, is a sure way to do it!

The breed you're dealing with certainly plays a significant part in the whole handling process as well. Some are more challenging to live with, while others justifiably have a reputation for being easy to handle. Most of the large breeds – such as Rhode Island Reds, Sussex, Orpington, Cochin and Brahma – fall into the latter category, displaying calm, docile natures by and large (but there are always exceptions). Although these birds can be physically quite big, there are bantam varieties available which are easier to manage, especially for inexperienced keepers. Nevertheless, it's always worth remembering that any chicken has the capacity to peck, scratch with its claws and flap its wings, any of which can cause injury to a handler.

Game birds are generally more aggressive by nature, and tend to be 'flighty' and excitable with it. But there are a number of soft feather breeds known for their flightiness too, including Leghorn and Hamburgh, which is inevitably going to make them rather more difficult to live with.

Handling is certainly something that all keepers should master and, while it's not difficult in theory, there are a number of essential ground rules to be learnt first. Attitude is important, but confidence is vital. It's also crucial for keepers with young families to emphasise the need for good handling technique to their children. Youngsters must be encouraged to hold the birds properly too. Gripping them tightly in a loving embrace – as they might do with a cat or a puppy – can be a recipe for disaster, and must be avoided if the birds are to remain unstressed and well-adjusted towards the idea of human interaction.

While this isn't something I'd recommend, it certainly illustrates how relaxed and safe a bird can be that's used to being handled

Cornering and catching chickens is a skill that all keepers need to master.
Handling your birds regularly is a vital part of any good husbandry
program, so everyone needs to develop skill and confidence with the
techniques involved

Catching is obviously the first requirement and, to be honest, there's a bit of an art to it. It's certainly something that takes

practice as well as a thoughtful approach. For the best, least disruptive results, you need to pick your moment carefully. Chickens

Be careful when making your final lunge for the bird. Avoid grabbing at
the neck. While ideally you should aim for the main body, a leg is often an
easy initial point of contact, but it should never be pulled or twisted

are easily upset and, once they become disturbed, their stress levels rise. While this may sound a trivial matter, it's potentially quite serious because birds under stress become less resistant to disease, and more prone to infection and other general ailments.

No rushing!

So the last thing you want to be doing is rushing around the pen like a mad thing, making repeated but unsuccessful lunges at your increasingly petrified hens! Of course, the type of breed you're dealing with plays a big part in how easy the birds are to catch. The large, docile types, like Cochins and Orpingtons (plus most hybrid layers), will normally be much simpler to pick up than those of a more flighty nature, such as the Leghorn or Spanish. Although these characteristic differences can be somewhat diluted by regular handling, they're always likely to remain to some degree.

All else being equal, the best time to attempt to handle a chicken is at night, once the birds have been settled in their house for an hour or two. They are most relaxed at this time and, therefore, easiest to pick up. This assumes, though, that you can get to them simply and without causing too much disturbance; the type of poultry house you have will play a big part in this. Large access doors make life a lot easier, meaning that you can get to the birds conveniently, slowly gathering and lifting the chosen bird off its perch with ease.

But if, for whatever reason, you need to catch one of your birds at any other time of the day then, depending on the situation, it can be more of a struggle. Free-range birds are obviously the most difficult to catch, as cornering them can be all but impossible. Chickens are no slouches when it comes to evading capture, and if you're dealing with one of the more mobile breeds then you'll have your work cut out.

Birds kept in a smaller run are easier to deal with but you still need to take care not to induce blind panic among the flock. So all your actions need to be measured and calm. Avoid sudden, unpredictable movements and

Careful use of an angler's landing net can represent a convenient way of catching smaller, more flighty birds. However, birds will quickly get to recognise it!

making loud noises. A clumsy and thoughtless approach at this stage can quickly undo all the good work you may have done towards 'taming' your hens previously.

Always approach your quarry slowly, trying your best to guide it into a corner where its escape options will be limited. Adopt a semi-crouching pose, with your

arms spread wide to either side. Then, when you feel you're within comfortable 'lunging range' make a swift and decisive grab for the bird. Do your best to get hold of the bird's body, and avoid grabbing at the neck. Try not to grab at a wing either as these are relatively easy to damage if you don't know what you're doing. If you catch hold of a leg, then quickly move your other hand on to the bird's body so you can you can then adjust your grip to the body with both hands. Never swing the bird up into the air by a leg because you may cause a dislocation, or even break a bone.

If you're not keen on this approach, then another option is to use a large net – the sort that anglers use is normally ideal. They typically have long handles that give you an impressive reach, and are light enough to remain manoeuvrable. The one problem is that the birds quickly get to recognise the net, and learn to associate the sight of it with the unfortunate experience of being forcibly caught.

Well balanced?

Once you've caught the bird it's important to calm it as quickly as possible, and the best way of doing this is to make it feel both comfortable and secure. Contrary to what you might imagine, a tight, smothering grip isn't the answer. A lot of novice keepers make the mistake of trying to hang on too tightly, either clutching the bird firmly to their chest with both arms, or gripping it, vice-like, under one. The bird will hate either, and will start flapping furiously at the first opportunity. This is potentially dangerous for both the bird and the 'holder'.

With all this in mind, it's very important to adjust your grip to something that the bird will feel comfortable with, as soon as you can. To do this, position one hand underneath the bird, so that your fingers run parallel with the breast bone and on past the legs. Place one or two fingers between the legs, and the remainder on either side, so that the legs can be gripped securely but without pinching them together (painful for the bird). Adopting this grip will mean that the bird feels balanced

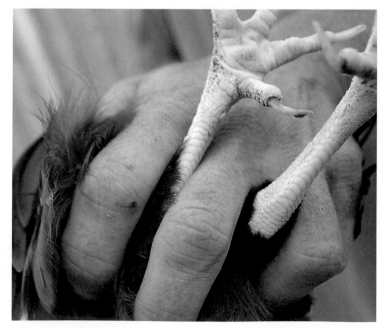

It's important to always place one or two fingers between a bird's legs when holding it, to ensure that the legs aren't squeezed painfully together as they are gripped

Plenty of support, and a balanced, level position, will ensure a bird rests happily on the hand

Facing the bird backwards, with head and neck under the carrying arm, is a convenient and unstressful way of moving birds over short distances

and secure, as its body is cradled in your hand. But it's important that your hand is level when holding the bird. It's no good if your grip is sloping the bird one way or the other; it'll feel insecure and will start to flap in panic. Sometimes a hand placed lightly on the bird's back can provide a useful, additional calming measure. Obviously, the bird's size has a bearing on how easy it is to hold in one hand like this – bantams aren't a problem, but the heavy breeds can be more of a challenge in terms of the strength needed to support their weight.

Extra support

Once the bird is settled, move your hand and the bird towards your body, so that one side rests against, and is supported by, you. This will enhance the feeling of security for the bird, and make it much easier to carry around. Obviously, though, If you have a long distance to move birds, it's always better to use a carrying box of some description – minimising stress for the bird and keeper!

Most experienced keepers adapt the hand-carrying method to suit themselves; my wife, for example, always favours carrying the bird as described above, but with it facing backwards and its neck under her arm, which always seems to keep them extremely calm.

Another thing that I find useful is to gently pat and stroke birds that I'm carrying. This is another great stress-reliever, and makes the whole process that much easier.

All in all, there are no great secrets to handling poultry; success essentially relies on a mixture of basic technique, confidence plus good, old-fashioned common sense. But it is something that should be got right. Good handling really is one of the husbandry basics and, as such, should be one of the first things that all keepers should master. But take your time and try not to get flustered when you start. If you think it'll help, go for a 'masterclass' with a breeder or experienced enthusiast nearby. Alternatively, join your local poultry society or club, and learn that way – remember that it's always much easier to pick-up techniques like this after a demonstration. •

A well-held bird will feel balanced and happy; there will be no flapping, no panic and no problem. Learning to do this is essential for all keepers

Shock tactics

One of the most effective methods available to you to keep the fox at bay is to install electric fencing. Chris Graham looks at what's involved

"I had a disaster last night... the fox got in with my chickens and savaged five of them. The carnage is horrible. I'm devastated!" This is just the sort of distressing situation that Bob Taylor and his staff deal with on a regular basis. He runs a company called Electric Fencing Direct Ltd (www.electricfencing.co.uk). For this reason he spends quite a bit of time consoling owners who've been faced with the devastating aftermath of just such an attack. It's just a shame that it takes the horror of such an experience to spur people into action when it comes to beefing up the protection levels for their birds.

One thing that everyone who keeps poultry should be aware of is that the fox is a cunning devil. The trouble is, they have time on their side; they can play the waiting game, all night, every night, for however long it takes! But it's not just rural owners who must be on their guard against these efficient predators. The 'urban' fox is, in many ways, an even more worthy adversary. Becoming ever more numerous in towns and cities, these creatures are streetwise, bold and confident.

Flexible posts mean netting fence is almost impossible to damage

Distress purchase

It's unfortunate, then, that so many poultry enthusiasts seem to wait until trouble strikes before taking action, particularly as the trouble in this case is normally so ghastly. Clearing up after the fox has called isn't something you ever want to do twice.

But keeping poultry safe in the domestic environment can throw up a few practical problems, particularly if you want to avoid that utilitarian 'prison camp' look. Owners who allow their birds to free-range in the garden, or in an orchard or paddock close to the house, tend not to want towering rigid metal fences spoiling the view. These ugly structures (usually capped with electrified wire) are necessary to ensure a fox-free environment, but both the financial and aesthetic costs can be high.

Electrified netting represents a far less visually intrusive, yet still extremely effective, alternative to eight-foot high wire fences. It provides a simple and convenient way of creating a free-range pen just about anywhere you want, without the 'eyesore' factor of a more permanent structure. The dark green lightweight plastic and wire strand construction blends into the surroundings and makes it easy to handle and completely flexible in terms of location; you can move the position of the enclosure as often as you like.

Of course, it would be wrong to suggest that an electrified netting fence provides a *guaranteed* barrier against foxes, and Bob's the first to admit that this is a claim he never makes. However, its protective powers are impressive. In the two years that Bob has been using this system with his own birds – he keeps a free-range laying flock of about 20 assorted birds – there have only been two occasions when there's been a problem with a fox – but in both instances the blame lay with Bob; he'd forgotten to switch

Electric fencing product choice is large, so Bob Taylor's Kit approach provides a simple option for all

on the power! And therein lies a weakness of the system.

Human error is the factor which is always going to represent the biggest potential threat. Forgetting to switch the power back on after you've been inside the pen or moving the netting is all too easy to do, and will leave the birds extremely vulnerable. To make things worse, foxes have the habit of cruelly exploiting such mistakes; they seem to have an uncanny sense for when the power is off.

Power options
Talking of power, there are basically two choices available – mains or battery – and there isn't much between them in cost terms for the basic set-ups. But some people find the idea of a mains-powered netting fence off-putting, imagining that it's going to be dangerous and difficult to deal with. In reality, the voltages pulsing through the netting are exactly the same with both power sources; the big difference is one of versatility. Battery-power systems are 'stand alone', which means they can be rigged up just about anywhere you like. This is in contrast to the plug-in systems which are limited by the need to be connected (using a low-resistance 'lead out' cable) to a mains power socket.

However, whichever power source is chosen, the final result is the same. Both systems work in conjunction with a clever device called an energiser. This is used to convert the input power (be it from a battery or the mains supply) into a high voltage, low amperage pulse that is forced around the live wires in the netting. The current involved – around 6,000 volts – sounds scarily high but there's actually little risk to health at a practical level. For a start, the fact that the current is pulsed, rather than being continuous, makes the fence 'safe' but uncomfortable to touch; it's equivalent to the sort of static

Making a gate using an extra fence post makes getting in and out of the run easy

Fence posts designed with 'tread-in' double prong are a great help when the ground is dry or frozen

A voltmeter is essential for monitoring system efficiency

shock commonly delivered from car doors at the end of a journey. What's more, the on/off nature of the current gives whatever's touching it the chance to recoil and break the contact before any damage is done.

Also, it's likely that the current pulsing around most fence circuits will be reduced to 3,000-4,000 volts due to natural wastage in the system. A good proportion of it will leak away to earth wherever contact is made. Bob says that to remain operationally effective the current flow should never be allowed to drop below the 3,000-volt mark, and this is an aspect which users must keep a constant check on using an electrical meter.

A further variation on the power theme offered by Electric Fencing Direct is the use of a small solar panel, which can be linked to the battery-powered systems in a couple of ways. The more complicated option sees the solar unit acting as a trickle charge unit which switches between a pair of batteries, charging one while the other powers the fence. Then, when the 'working' battery gets low on charge, the system switches automatically, the charged battery becomes the power source and the spent one is then charged up again by the solar panel. The alternative utilises just one battery that's linked permanently to the solar panel and is trickle-charged continuously. This system can run for up to nine months before the battery will have to be disconnected and given a thorough recharge.

Straight talking

One of the most appealing aspects of an electrified netting fence is its locational flexibility. However, to ensure the most effective performance there are a few important practical aspects to bear in mind.

Most obviously the fence must be a 'tight fit' with the ground otherwise foxes will find it easy to push their way underneath; a particular problem if the ground is uneven or rutted. Netting of the sort Bob supplies features 12 horizontal strands that carry wires and are electrified (all the vertical strands are plastic so don't carry a charge). But it's important to note that the bottom horizontal strand isn't live, and is purely intended to provide convenient anchorage between the posts. Hooks are used to peg down the netting, and their spacing is determined by the contour of the ground.

Keeping the fence more or less vertical is another important practical factor. Most systems rely on the use of plastic posts which are lightweight, durable and

GOOD MAINTENANCE

- *Inspect netting daily*
- *Ensure 3,000V+ at all times*
- *Keep weeds and grass cut back*
- *Never strim close to netting*
- *Take care when pegging out*
- *Listen for tell-tale electrical clicking denoting loss to earth*
- *Maintain netting tension*
- *Reposition leaning posts*

Stand-alone systems use 12-volt leisure/caravan batteries rather than automotive units. They offer great portability and operational flexibility, but do need to be regularly charged

convenient. However, they're flexible too and this can make it difficult to create the tension that's needed to keep the netting upright. EFD's solution is to provide simple guy ropes which are used on each of the enclosure's corner posts. If necessary, specially-made net struts are available to provide tension on the longer runs.

Specifying the right system for any given situation has traditionally been a bit of a problem. Most catalogues are groaning with energiser and battery options and you may find there's simply too much choice; it can all be very confusing for the beginner. EDF take all the guesswork out of the purchasing process by offering a range of all-inclusive kits based on nothing more complicated than the number of birds owned. So, for example, the standard 50m Kit is suitable for keepers with 2-7 birds, and is available in battery or mains-powered versions.

Each kit includes an appropriate length of netting (with bound-in posts), all necessary pegs and fixings, a carefully matched energiser, all electrical cabling and connections, an external on/off switch, a net repair kit, full instructions and – last but not least – an 'Electric Fence' warning sign. ●

Solar panel being set up to keep a battery-powered system charged

Thwarting Mr Fox

Mike Woolnough considers allotment hens and the ever-present threat of foxes

Most people seem to regard foxes as nocturnal animals, but this simply isn't the case – particularly with urban foxes. I have often seen them out on our allotments as late as 10am, and as early as three in the afternoon.

Town foxes have to work that much harder to find food and, if you don't watch out, your lovely, plump allotment hen will be top choice on the menu. One pair raised six cubs among the overgrown brambles in the corner of our field last year, and the parents were out and about at all hours trying to find food for them. They successfully reared all six, but the brambles have now been cleared so, hopefully, they'll have moved on to annoy somebody else now.

Most of the poultry fanciers on our allotments have lost birds, and some have been hit several times. You only have to look at their housing and runs, though, to see

This allotment hen keeper listened very carefully to all advice before building his chicken housing, and created an almost perfect set-up. There's a fully-enclosed, covered back run that's weatherproof (and complies with Avian Influenza prevention requirements), coupled with two front outdoor runs. His birds are periodically switched from one side to the other, allowing the ground to recover and grow fresh grass. This is known as the Balfour System, but he slightly spoiled its effectiveness by keeping too many birds for the area available. The steel fencing panels are augmented by underground perimeter wire netting, and topped-off with heavy-duty rope netting

the weak points. I don't mind because while the fox is getting an easy meal from their premises, it isn't going to waste time trying to crack my chicken run defences.

When I built our first run I was absolutely paranoid about foxes, and I made it harder to crack than Alcatraz. For the house I used an 8x6ft/2.5x1.8m timber shed, standing on concrete slabs. The wood was slightly rotten in places so, knowing that a fox can easily chew through soft wood, I reinforced large areas with larch lap fencing nailed on the outside. Unfortunately, this subsequently turned out to be a wonderful haven for red mite, but you live and learn!

The run was constructed of 3in/75mm square timber posts clad with 6ft/1.8m-high chicken wire. This mesh was also stretched over the top, with all the pieces very carefully wired together so there were no gaps anywhere. It was a work of art, and the result of many hours' careful labour. The *pièce de resistance* was the floor of the run; I removed all the soil to a depth of six inches and then spread chain link fencing flat over the whole area. This was also all carefully stitched together with wire, and then all the soil was brought back

An allotment generally allows you to give your stock more space than at home. Here our Coronation and Light Sussex large fowl enjoy a scratch round in the straw looking for a handful of corn thrown to them

Our first run was bombproof! I nailed a strong wire to the tops of the posts, then the top edge of the side wire and the edges of the roofing were carefully wired to it using a kind of running stitch of finer wire. No gaps were left anywhere

in and spread back over the top. Finally I added a deep layer of leaf mould across the entire run, which the chickens loved to scratch and hunt in for the handful of corn that I threw in each morning.

Something like this is a great idea in permanently fixed runs, as it helps to keep them fresh and prevents the formation of mud baths in bad weather. The covering is constantly topped-up and, once a year, the whole top layer is dug out and added to the compost heap. This wonderful mix of rotted leaves, chicken droppings and decomposed, uneaten weeds is just about the most potent soil treatment you can make. The local council clear up large quantities of fallen leaves in autumn from the allotments and adjoining parks, and is happy to dump them in our leaf stores. Last year's very wet autumn messed up all the arrangements though, and we didn't get any leaves at all. So this year we're having to use a layer of wheat straw. The chickens seem to like it just as well, but it won't break down so quickly for compost.

Chicken sense

I mentioned weeds in the run, but I wasn't referring to ones growing there – the hens very quickly polish those off – but to the heaps that get *thrown* in there. With four allotments we dig up a mountain of weeds, and the whole lot get dumped into the chicken runs for them to pick over. Obviously, I watch out for *bella donna* (Deadly Nightshade) but, other than that, I don't worry. My experience is that the birds have enough sense not to eat those plants that are supposed to be dangerous for them (such as groundsel) but, even if they do, I reckon the dangers are overstated. Mine get everything and have had no problems, and if I happen to throw in an armful of chickweed... well, it's like the rush for the January sales!

My security-conscious approach was probably overkill, but the fact remains that it works and this first run has never been breached by Mr Fox. I later added heavier gauge, small-holed wire around the base of the run, after I found out that badgers could chew straight

through standard chicken wire with ease. Luckily, I learnt this from a book, rather than finding out the hard way.

Having done a lot more research, our next run was built very differently, partly because the cost of the posts and chicken wire was high, but also because we discovered a much quicker and easier way of doing things. We found out that steel construction site fencing is often available cheaply after a building project is finished, and slightly damaged 11ft/3.3m sections typically cost about £10 each. Six of these make an excellent 22x11ft/6.6x3.3m chicken run that's quite easy to erect.

A fox can dig under this fencing in a matter of minutes though, so you need to deal with that threat. With the fence in place, dig a trench 6-12in/0.15m-0.3m deep and 12in/0.3m wide right around the perimeter. Then run wire netting all around the run, taking it down into the trench and flat across the bottom of it, before back-filling with soil. Foxes always dig directly at the base of a fence – not at a distance from it – so they will always hit this sort of submerged barrier and then give up. I've often arrived on the allotments to be met by a heap of soil and a hole, so I know the system works. But note that it doesn't matter what type of wire netting you use, just bear in mind that it'll rust. We prefer to use chain link fencing as you can often buy second hand rolls of it very cheaply at auctions, and it's extremely strong – even a badger wouldn't get past it.

Expansion plans

These first two runs were built about 8ft/2.5m apart and, eventually, I decided to infill and make another run by building new fences across both ends, bridging to the shed at the front end. I duly sank chain link into the ground at the base of both these fences and considered it 'job done'. But a few months later I went to the allotments early in the morning to feed and water our stock, and found a hole going under the shed. I smiled to myself and thought: "Ha–ha, you probably gave yourself a headache when you hit the concrete slabs, mate!"... but then I spotted feathers lying around.

The crafty blighter had dug right under the corner of the shed and come up in the infill run before nipping into the henhouse. As luck would have it, he only took one out

As long as the roof area of your run is completely covered and secure, it doesn't really matter what it looks like. I used nylon trawler netting stretched tightly across ours, with the edges securely tied in place

of 20 of our lovely buff Sussex bantams, which was a real let-off. Foxes will usually go on a killing spree, slaughtering everything that moves, and it's this behaviour that's given rise to the idea that they kill for fun. I don't believe this because, if left undisturbed, they will return repeatedly to remove each carcass, one by one. After one allotment holder lost 17 birds in one night they were all discovered hurriedly buried at points all over the field.

The last vulnerable spot is the roof, or rather a lack of it. Believe it or not, a fox can scramble its way over a 6ft/1.8m high fence, and so some further protection is required. I was lucky enough to buy a truly huge roll of nylon trawler netting three years ago for 20 quid. It's been used to cover a 20ft/6m poly tunnel, various vegetable cages, all my chicken run, and I've still got plenty left! It's as tough as old boots and has many practical uses. Any strong netting will do to cover your run but, be warned that when it's wet you'll get a soaking if you happen to nudge it from underneath!

If you can't cover your run, then you really need to build the sides higher than six feet – ideally about

eight. Also, don't forget that the pile of wood you've stacked beside the run, or the nice raised vegetable bed, will be used as a stepladder by a wily fox to give him a leg-up over your fencing. One chap on our allotments lost his stock after the fox used his compost heap as a springboard. I found fox droppings in our goat run when I stacked a dismantled shed beside it, and can only imagine that the fox used the piled-up pallets of the goats' adventure playground as a means of escape afterwards – they really are amazingly acrobatic.

Incidentally, there are many old tales regarding keeping foxes away from your stock. One that I've heard is that if you pour human urine around the perimeter of your chicken run, you'll effectively establish it as your territory and foxes won't come near. Well, it's poppycock! I found that they immediately leave droppings everywhere to re-mark it as their territory!

So, don't be put off by the threat of a fox attack on your allotment chicken run; just think the whole thing through carefully, take sensible precautions, and you and your birds will be fine.
•

Taking adequate precautions when you build their run should ensure a long, happy and safe life for your allotment hens

Keeper's nightmare

John Newsome offers some practical advice for on understanding and dealing with the significant threat posed by mink, weasels, stoats and ferrets

Above: The mink may look cute and cuddly, but it's a very effective killer too. If you live near running water then it's always going to be a threat

Most people who keep poultry for any length of time are likely to have lost birds to a member of the *mustelidae* family – that's mink, stoats, weasels and feral ferrets to you and me!

The ability of these creatures to squeeze though the smallest opening, or scale the highest fence, coupled with their destructive tendencies towards poultry, means a visit is likely to generate heartbreak and extreme frustration for any poultry keeper.

Greatest damage

The potential for damage is greatest from the larger minks and ferrets, whether they are released pets or descended from fur farm escapees. Unfortunately, though, securing your poultry run against these crafty predators is all but impossible. Mink and ferrets are perfectly capable of squeezing in through the holes left by gnawing rats, while the smaller weasels and stoats will happily make use of mouse holes to gain entry. Once inside a hen house, these predators have the ruthless ability to kill any number of birds they find there and, if some remain, returning to finish them off later.

Consequently, this is definitely one of those situations when prevention is better than cure. The most efficient and time-saving method of controlling these pests is the use of a fen trap, although I should stress that it's vital to use the correct size to guarantee a quick and painless death. Under the Spring Traps Approval Orders 1995, fen traps of size Mark IV are suitable for weasels or stoats, while the larger *mustelidae* – such as mink or ferrets – should be trapped in a size Mark VI.

Fen traps are available from most feed merchants and only cost around £10. However, the big problem with them is that they are indiscriminate, and have the potential to catch and kill anything that happens to trigger them. For this reason it's very important to place the fen trap inside a specially constructed tunnel (required if the trap is to be sited in the open, by UK law), which is easily built using scrap wood with appropriately sized entrance holes to restrict access to all but the intended

Many regard 'live traps' like this as being a more humane option, but using one leaves you with the problem of what to do with the creature once you've caught it

A weasel like this will happily make use of mouse holes as entry points into poultry houses, so keeping them out can be extremely difficult with older structures

victims. It's actually illegal to site one of these traps where it may potentially harm a protected animal, such as a passing badger. The tunnels, as well as being a requirement under UK law, also appeal to the generally secretive nature of these predators, which can boost their effectiveness no end. Another benefit is that they may well also catch rats too.

Fen traps need to be checked every day, and you should make this part of your poultry husbandry

If you find dead birds with their heads missing, then this can be a classic sign of an attack by a mink, or a ferret like this one

routine. This is another legal requirement, to prevent potential animal suffering if a victim is caught but not killed. This is an aspect that puts some people off but, unfortunately, there's no easy way to deal with these destructive creatures. I'm afraid that violence is inevitably going to be involved, somewhere down the line. If you don't fancy dealing with traps then I suppose you may be able to find somebody who will do it for you (make enquiries through your local poultry club or society, or perhaps contact a local game keeper). There's nothing like experience for knowing how best to deal with this kind of problem!

Further options

Another option would be to shoot the animal; although usually attacking at night, they can also be quite brazen about what they're doing. This means that you may get the chance to shoot or, alternatively, attack the perpetrator with a weapon such as a broom stick or other handy piece of timber. In my experience, it's often worth carrying a length of 2x4in with you for this very purpose, as you're examining the disaster area. There's nothing more frustrating than watching a mink wave at you from the bottom of a run while you're unable to do anything about it.

However, in those cases where you're simply presented with the aftermath of an attack, and there's no sign of the perpetrator, then it's important that you prioritise; concentrate on the remaining, healthy birds. It's rare that the attackers will merely injure a victim

– they're too efficient for that. So give each survivor a quick, all-over check as you move them to alternative accomodation. Also be sure to check them all before proceeding to the vet; the last bird you catch and inspect may be the worst.

But before you set off for the vet, consider this; the chances are that if the intruder ate some of its catch, it'll be sleeping-off its meal close by, and could return at any moment. So be sure not to leave any live birds at the scene of the attack. Unpleasant though it may be, it can be a smart move to leave behind a dead bird or two, as 'easy pickings' for the returning predator. Hopefully, this may be enough to dissuade it from going on a fresh search for more live prey.

Another unfortunate reality is that once one of these creatures strikes, the chances are that it'll either expand its territory nearer to you or, worse still, establish a new one close by especially to take advantage of the food that's conveniently 'on offer'. Obviously, this will make its capture even more of a priority, as the visits will only become more frequent as long as you have birds it can take.

At this point you have two choices; 'dead catch' or 'live catch' traps. The latter option, while perhaps appearing a less drastic measure, presents an immediate problem about what to do with the animal if you catch one. It's now an offence to release a ferret or mink back into the wild. It's also irresponsible to simply move the problem on so that it affects some other unsuspecting poultry keeper.

A fen trap like this is a dangerous device and must be very carefully handled and sited. Never use them in the open; not only will this be ineffective at catching the intended victim, it will also risk other pets and wildlife

The right trap?

Live traps are widely available from specialist suppliers (from about £30), but it's important to note that many aren't designed to contain stoats and weasels. These animals will often be able to get in and out, taking the bait, at will. My advice is to talk with a knowledgeable specialist, or use the Internet to research exactly what you need. When using one of these traps, it's best to remove any dead birds from the area and place a small quantity of fresh poultry meat in the trap to act as bait. Preparation before an attack often pays dividends at this point. Having traps 'in stock' which have been stored close buy and have lost their 'newness' will mean that they're likely to be more effective. Although mink, weasels, ferrets and stoats tend not to be as naturally wary as rats – and, consequently, easier to trap – there are still rules to be followed.

An understanding of the target animal's behavior is a valuable asset. Members of the *mustelidae* family tend to travel around the edges of open spaces. They feel more secure doing this, and will rarely cross wide open spaces. Consequently, potentially good trap sites include under sheds or along their edges, in ditches, along the base of walls and hedgerows. The same general rules apply when setting traps inside a building – go for the corners or edges; don't

Putting a fen trap inside a home-made 'tunnel' makes it both more effective and safer to use

simply place the trap in the centre of an open space.

Using a hand-made tunnel for containing the trap always helps, as does disguising it with pieces of turf. In fact, turf can usefully be used to channel the animals right

Using old, unpainted scrap wood for the tunnel is important – brand new or treated materials will tend to put-off predators. It's also very important to cut the access hole size accurately to match the target animal

into the trap if you have discovered its point of entry into the shed or hen house.

If you've no choice but to use brand new traps, then you can lessen the impact by sprinkling few fresh pine needles around to help mask the smell of new paint and packaging etc. It also makes a lot of sense to set more than just one trap, to increase your chances of a catch. It's not unknown for adult females to take their maturing youngsters on hunting raids into a hen house, so the more traps there are, the better.

Know your enemy

So how do you know which animal is actually taking your livestock? Well, there are a few useful clues to spot. For example, if you discover that smaller birds are being killed first, and just little bits of flesh are being consumed, then this suggests that you're dealing with a stoat or weasel attack (although I have heard of these animals taking birds as big as half-grown geese).

Large quantities of flesh being consumed and, in particular, the removal of the head, is typical of the actions of a mink or feral ferret, although it's a common trait of the *mustelidae* family of predators to bite the area at the base of the skull – it quickly disables large and potentially dangerous prey. There is a distinct difference between rat and *mustelidae* attacks, Typically, rats will only attack broody hens, chicks and small bantams, and this can be more common if you regularly feed pellets; these are a big attraction for rats.

Mink are, by inclination, semi-aquatic so if you live near running water then bear this in mind. They really are very ferocious predators, and rarely leave anything alive following an attack within the confines of a hen house. If you find that birds are being killed outside during the day, then you can use these as bait to hopefully help catch the offender when it returns. If you can move a carcass or two to the base of a nearby wall or shed, so much the better. Stake them down so they can't be dragged away, then place and disguise a trap nearby, which the predator will hopefully visit as it returns for another meal. •

Dealing with rodents

Terry Beebe provides ten points to consider when having to deal with rats and mice

Above: Rats pose a serious threat to chickens and their keepers; your poultry will attract them and they must be controlled

Keeping poultry at home means that, unfortunately, you're also more than likely to be 'keeping' rodents too! The bottom line is that chickens – and everything that goes with them – attract rats, mice and squirrels.

Unfortunately, all three have the potential to cause problems for poultry enthusiasts and their birds. Here's my ten-point summary of the best ways to keep the situation under control.

1 Know your enemy

The rat (*Rattus norvegicus*; the Norwegian rat) is without doubt the most destructive and dangerous member of the rodent family we have to deal with. Although it arrived in the UK from Denmark, the species actually originated in China. Now, of course, it has spread worldwide, and is one of nature's great survivors.

The mouse (*Mus musculus*), although a lot smaller than the common rat, is also perfectly capable of causing chaos inside and around your poultry sheds. Never write them off as inconsequential just because they're cuddlier than rats!

Squirrels, although attractive and often encouraged into gardens and fed by many people, tend to be more annoying than actually damaging. While they can certainly wreak havoc among your garden plants and bulbs, they can also cause structural and electrical damage to poultry houses, sheds and barns.

Remember that all rodents are capable of carrying disease and so, as a general rule, it's best to wear gloves when handling items which may have been contaminated by any of these animals.

2 Where are they?

Poultry houses and runs offer just about the ideal living and breeding conditions for rodents. Rats and mice love nothing better than quiet, dark spaces in which to thrive, which is why sheds, barns and chicken houses offer such welcoming sanctuary. The additional benefit of living around poultry is that there's always a ready supply of food on hand.

A hen house which sits directly on the ground, or just a few inches

Squirrels are certainly less problematic, but are avid feed stealers and can cause structural damage too

Picking up a sack of feed that's had its base chewed out is frustrating to say the least...

As I've already mentioned, there's also the risk of them chewing through electrical insulation and causing fires, plus there are all the social problems associated with attracting rats in an urban environment. Once neighbours make a link between your birds and a rodent infestation – whether it's justified or not – there's bound to be trouble.

Rodents love to nest in quiet, undisturbed places. So clear away old piles of wood and never leavesacks of feed like this; they are a rat magnet!

above it, presents an irresistible environment offering dry, warm shelter; ideal for nesting and breeding. Most rodents are excellent at burrowing, and master chewers too. They will gnaw their way into virtually any cavity, and can climb almost anything.

Rats and mice will also take advantage of the secure shelter offered by old wood piles, neglected compost heaps and paving stone paths; all these provide potential nesting sites that you need to be aware of. Rats will dig and chew their way through virtually anything. I've seen them gnaw through a one-inch thick poultry shed floor, creating a four-inch diameter hole through which they then started dragging out young growers.

3 What are the problems?
One of the greatest nuisances caused by rodents is when they raid poultry feed bins or sacks. Metal containers really are the only secure answer to this. If you don't use these, then at least get your containers off the floor to make things more difficult for them.

4 Danger times
There are certain times of the year when rodent problems become much more apparent. Winter is one of them, when rats and mice actively seek out warmth and shelter – chicken houses can offer both. Also, at harvest time, once farmers begin working in the fields, our four-legged friends are forced to seek quieter accommodation, and back gardens can be ideal. However, the relatively mild weather we've had over the past few years means that rodents are becoming a year-round threat.

A female rat produces up to five litters a year, giving birth to as many as 14 youngsters at a time. The period of pregnancy is just 21 days. The average lifespan is three years, but most rats rarely manage to survive more than one. Interestingly, rats have the ability to adjust their reproduction rates to balance their numbers. So, if large numbers in a colony are killed off, the remainder compensate with increased birth rates.

Typical rat damage to the floor of a hen house

The mouse has a reproductive cycle of 20 days, and produces litters of around 10-12. The babies grow very quickly, and can themselves start breeding after about 50 days.

5 Human trouble

Both rats and mice carry diseases which, by and large, tend to represent more of a threat to us than they do to our birds. The rat is famous as a spreader of the very unpleasant Weil's disease, as well as cryptosporidiosis and viral hemorrhagic fever. These are all potentially serious diseases, which can affect both animals and humans; Weil's is probably the most common of them.

Rats were blamed for Bubonic Plague (Black Death), although this is actually most often transmitted by fleas living on them. The rat itself remains immune.

Mice carry very similar parasites, but are rarely responsible for the diseases already mentioned. However, it's important to avoid breathing in dust which may have come into contact with mouse droppings, as this can be a source hantavirus, another extremely unpleasant and dangerous condition.

These sorts of disease tend to be contracted following contact with rodent droppings or urine, so always make sure you wear gloves, protective clothing and a facemask where appropriate. Gloves are especially essential if you have a cut or broken skin on your hands.

Squirrels can also carry disease, but it's rare for them to pose any direct threat to humans.

6 Control methods

Effective rodent control is very important nowadays. The law states that you are legally required to keep any form of rodent under control, and eradicate as required. The fact that these troublesome creatures breed with such vigour means that keeping them under control is a constant battle.

Popular methods to use include traps ('live catch' or 'impact') or poison. The latter comes in various forms, but all must be used very carefully to avoid harming yourself and other wildlife or pets in the vicinity. Recently, environmentally-friendly, corn-based baits have

come on to the market which, although lethal to rodents, pose no threat at all to anything else. These, as you might imagine, are becoming increasingly popular with poultry keepers.

But whatever control method you choose, it's important to appreciate that half the battle involves keeping your immediate environment as unfriendly to rodents as possible. So clear away piles of rubbish, old wood and logs, make sure your hen houses are raised a foot or so off the ground, don't allow spilt feed to hang around on the ground, check and turn compost heaps regularly, secure feed bins and other stores, avoid the use of paving slabs whenever possible.

The use of traps is an alternative to poisons, but it inevitably brings the creatures 'up close and personal', which many people prefer to avoid. Impact traps are designed to kill the victim instantly and, usually they do. Sometimes they don't, however. 'Live catch' traps, obviously, catch the animal without harming it. But what do you do with it then?

There is a variety of traps available, ranging from the ferocious, old-style Gin trap, with serrated metal jaws, to the newer, ready-baited types that are simplicity itself to use. These have a covered centre pod containing the bait, and are simply set by removing the cover and pressing the rear to open the jaws.

7 Trap placement

There's an art to placing traps. Rats, in particular, are cunning creatures; naturally suspicious and very wary of change. Consequently, shiny new traps are often given a very wide berth, and can have no effect at all. So it's best to get a new trap dirty before setting it; bury it in the compost, cover it in earth or drag it around inside your poultry house, then leave it outside for a few days to remove the 'newness'.

If you've actually seen rats on your property (or signs of fresh digging), then place the trap at the point where you spotted them. Don't site it in the open, though; pick somewhere sheltered and out of sight, such as behind a leaning slab, round the back of a shed etc.

Trap placement is a bit of an art; they must be craftily positioned otherwise they'll have no effect

Bait used in live traps needs to be placed in a container inside the wire structure, so that it can only be eaten from inside. Ideal baits include peanut butter, molasses or a Mars bar – all are effective, easy to get and safe to use.

8 What works best?

Anti-coagulant bait will kill very quickly, in most cases a single feed will cause death. But the fact that this substance will also kill any other small animal or bird that eats it means that great care is needed. It must be very carefully placed somewhere with restricted access so

Putting poison directly down a freshly-dug hole is an effective method, but be sure to cover the opening afterwards to prevent other animals or pets getting at it

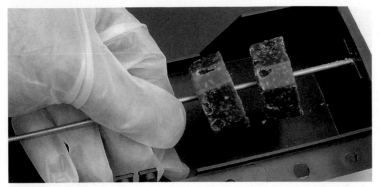

Wax-type bait blocks are a neat and safe anti-rodent measure when used inside a secure bait box like this

Ready-baited impact traps are convenient and easy to use, once the bait pod's cover has been removed

that only the intended victims can reach it – a secure bait station is the ideal solution.

I've used most makes of poison, including Roban, Rodex, Tom Cat, Neosorexa and Eradibait. All these, apart from Eradibait, are chemical-based, work quickly (kill after 1-4 days), but present a potential risk to other creatures.

Wax block baits, mounted on a rod fitted inside a secure box, have varying degrees of effectiveness, but can offer a safer alternative to the out-and-out chemical poisons.

The 'bait' used inside a wire 'live trap' like this must be placed in a solid container, so that the rodent has to enter the trap to get at it. We're using peanut butter in this example

9 How to kill

Dealing with a rat caught in a 'live trap' is no easy matter and it's the prospect of this which understandably puts many people off using these traps.

There are now strict animal welfare-related guidelines about the humane dispatching of rodents. You're allowed to shoot or kill them with a single blow to the head. However, drowning is certainly not classed as humane nowadays; you can be prosecuted for using this method under the protection of animals act 1911. It's these problems which push most people down the poison route as the favoured control method.

10 Final disposal

There are guidelines relating to rodent carcass disposal too. The official method requires you to wrap the body in a plastic bag, secure it and then place this inside a rigid plastic container which can then be disposed of in the refuse.

Never forget that, even when dead, rodents can still pose a disease threat, so always wear protective gloves and sensible clothing when handling them. •

There's a good range of rodent poisons and baits on the market. These are some I can recommend from experience

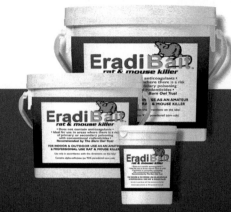

Lottie hens!

If you are thinking about keeping a few hens on your local allotment, then Mike Woolnough's practical experience is sure to help

The trend towards ethical food is leading to more and more people keeping a few hens on their allotments. They're so popular where we are that the whole place has a 'shanty town' feel to it

When you keep chickens in your garden, particularly if it's small, one of the biggest problems (other than predators) is disposing of old floor litter and chicken droppings.

Move your hens to an allotment, and this problem goes away since other gardeners want the waste for their compost – though it's likely you'll have none to spare as you will be composting it yourself to help raise your own tasty vegetables! Okay, that's only a minor benefit, but there are many more. You do, however, have to go

into keeping allotment chooks with a completely different mental attitude than you'd have for birds kept at home.

First things first though; you have to find an allotment field that has vacancies, and allows the keeping of chickens – not a particularly easy task in some areas these days. The growth of the 'green movement' brought about by the many television programmes regarding ethical food production has caused a severe shortage of allotment space, and waiting lists are quite common.

Also of importance is a water supply on your chosen field – some don't have taps and this will make chicken rearing (as well as vegetable irrigation) much harder. Working away from your home facilities is difficult enough without adding to the problems.

The first step should be to ring your local council to ask about allotment vacancies, to confirm whether hens are allowed and to check the water supply situation. Then, once you have the contact details for the secretary of a likely field, my advice is to ask to see the vacant plots, explaining that you'd like to grow some vegetables. Don't mention the chickens at this stage. Many secretaries have a built-in antipathy towards poultry on their field, as they probably cause more problems for them than anything else!

However, don't go into this imagining that you can simply use the whole plot for one massive chicken run; it's likely that you'll be expected to use a certain percentage of your land for raising crops. Admittedly, this isn't the case on all fields but you should, at least, be prepared to get a backache and muddy boots from sowing seeds and weeding! All fields have a strict policy about uncultivated plots, and if you let yours grow wild, you'll receive a written warning or two and then be evicted.

Another thing to bear in mind is that you are very unlikely to be permitted to keep cockerels. As far as I know, there are no councils that allow them, although many turn a blind eye if there are no complaints received from adjoining houses. On our field, the previous secretary ignored them unless they were a nuisance, but his successor is applying the rules and not allowing any new chicken keepers to have them. Luckily, he has chosen not to do anything about *existing* cockerels, which is a relief as ours are essential to our Sunday roast dinner production line! I was recently interviewed on the allotment by BBC Radio Suffolk, and one of my cockerels was crowing very ostentatiously in the background. I didn't even notice him but, listening to the broadcast set me praying that nobody from the council heard it!

One big advantage for 'lottie hens' is that they will, almost certainly, get more space than they would do at home, unless you have a large garden. Our first poultry run on our original plot (we have four plots now, totalling a quarter of an acre) was 15x10ft/4.5x3m, with an 8x6ft/2.5x1.8m garden shed as housing.

Almost everybody who keeps poultry on an allotment uses old garden sheds for housing; there's just no point whatsoever in buying a fancy and expensive hen house. In a domestic setting, of course, you

Most 'allotmenteers' use garden sheds for their chicken housing – they're so easy to convert. Red mite is a constant worry, so I spray regularly to keep it at bay

want the housing to be attractive and a feature of your garden, but on an allotment it's functionality and ruggedness that count.

Remember that anything attractive, and therefore expensive, is very likely to be stolen, or at least vandalised. I've even heard terrible tales of chicken houses, complete with their inhabitants, being burned down. I must stress that this is generally rare, but it's best to enquire about any past problems before you make your mind up and start building.

Make your house and run as secure as possible. Standard chicken wire is often OK in your garden, but solid chain link fencing is advisable out in the open. We now

Using a bowl of warm water to defrost a frozen drinker is the best method I've come across. Being impatient and trying to force open a frozen unit will almost certainly cause the plastic to shatter

construct all our new runs using the big steel fencing sections that you see around building sites. They are fairly easy to obtain secondhand, and very quick to erect. Whichever you use, you need to stretch some half-inch chicken wire around the bottom to stop the birds from poking their heads out, or chicks from escaping, and also to help prevent entry by vermin.

Yes, I'm afraid that vermin are another problem, generally much more so than in your garden. The many old sheds and dilapidated structures that are common on allotments provide warm accommodation for colonies of mice that'll happily welcome the free food on offer in a new chicken run. Rats can also be a problem, of course. Any that are spotted around your runs are sure to generate complaints at the council offices. So it's essential to keep all your feed sacks inside secure metal dustbins, as rats can gnaw through plastic ones with ease. If you scatter 'scratch' feed into your runs, then make sure that you only give a quantity that the birds will have eaten before nightfall. Also, suspend all feeders rather than stand them on the floor.

One advantage of using big sheds is that there's plenty of room for large feeders and drinkers which will keep your birds supplied for longer periods, and thus allow you to have a holiday. We've been away for a week at a time with no problems at all – although it's a good idea to get a neighbouring plot holder to collect the eggs or you may come home to find a very broody hen sitting atop a mountain of them!

You should be prepared to bring your own water supplies during spells of very icy weather. The lottie taps will almost certainly be turned off at the start of winter and, even if they're not, they'll freeze up solid at times. Your drinkers will also freeze, and we all know that these are difficult to unblock. The answer is a jerry can full of hot water and a washing up bowl. Stand the frozen drinker in the bowl and pour in some hot water. Go off and do your other jobs such as filling feeders and collecting eggs, and when you get back the drinker will be thawed out and ready for refilling. •

BEGINNERS' STORIES

New friends

Peter Hedley-Smith has been keeping chickens for just over six months, but he's already completely hooked on the hobby!

Seven newcomers to keeping chickens tell their own stories

Peter Hedley-Smith with the first hen, Holly

Have you ever thought of keeping chickens? I suspect that you might have, and that's probably why you're reading this book! That was me nine months ago, before the media decided that keeping poultry at home was trendy and a worthwhile pastime in these days of shrinking family budgets.

Like many beginners, I was unsure where to start. I didn't know what was involved, or exactly what I needed. Nevertheless, I had a burning desire to learn, and a great enthusiasm for this exciting new hobby. I had space at the bottom of the garden that was overgrown and serving no obvious purpose. I was also keen to start enjoying a supply of healthy, fresh eggs and to share the fun of hens pecking around in the garden. Now, not even a year on at the time of writing, I've certainly been hooked by the hobby.

Hatching a plan

My first move in the quest for knowledge was to turn to *Practical Poultry*, which provided excellent information on chicken and equipment suppliers. I also did some online research, and bought some useful, practical books on home poultry keeping.

But I still had a number of unanswered questions, so decided to book myself on a one-day course at The Domestic Fowl Trust in the Cotswolds. This was well worthwhile as it gave me an opportunity to see, first hand, a wide range of equipment and more than 120 types of rare breed chickens, ducks, geese and other fowl. I also visited a couple of poultry housing suppliers, to help with the decision-making process regarding the coop I needed.

I concluded the area available in the garden was large enough to accommodate six chickens, and that these birds would be perfectly capable of producing enough eggs for my family of five. I'd also decided that I preferred a permanent coop option to the moveable ark alternative. Importantly, the site was sufficiently sheltered to give shade in the summer, and protection from harsh winds in the winter.

As I cleared the nettles and

The poultry run was cleared from an area of unused scrub at the bottom of our garden. There's enough room for six birds and I raised the hen house eight inches off the ground as a deterrent to rats

brambles, I could see that I needed to replace a large section of wooden fencing. This bordered two sides of the enclosure, and I fenced the remainder with 1.2m chicken wire of a small enough gauge (25mm) to prevent the hens from getting their heads trapped.

I fitted a gravel board to the fencing base to deter any digging under, and was also confident that I'd be able to deter any rats by keeping waste food to a minimum (feeder stands have helped greatly). I also took the precaution of raising the coop eight inches (20.3cm) off the ground, to stop rats living under it. Lastly, being very much aware of the responsibility involved, I made sure that my neighbours would be happy to look after the hens if I was on holiday or away for a day or two.

Gail and **Prince!**

Getting broody

As I prepared the enclosure, my thoughts turned to what variety of chickens to buy. Did I want to keep them for their eggs or meat? I quickly decided I'd probably be unable to eat chickens that I'd lovingly looked after, so I looked at pure breed and hybrid types. I liked the traditional appearance of the pure breeds, even though they generally produce fewer eggs than the hybrids. I wanted family-friendly hens, and ones that weren't too flighty or difficult to keep. I made contact with a few local breeders to ask about point-of-lay hens but, being the middle of the year, stocks were low at that time. Nevertheless, I busied myself by ordering the poultry house, feeder and drinker (sufficient for a week's supply for up to six hens), feed, grit, sawdust, powders and disinfectants.

Everything was soon ready and the day arrived when my family and I were due to go and get our first birds. I was unsure about what to expect, and soon found myself gazing into a mix of sheds and runs containing several different types of chicken. First impressions were not good as the houses were dark and dirty. Some hens showed obvious signs of having been pecked and I saw enough there to put me off the idea of buying anything at all.

My youngest stepson was keen to buy a Black Rock but none of the hens looked healthy. The family were now getting fidgety when I spotted a few Light Sussex hens in another shed. I was assured that these were close to point-of-lay, and were about 12 weeks old. I still had my doubts and we eventually left with just one of the Light Sussex hens.

We returned home with our delicate cargo in an old cardboard box, and I put the bird into the new coop, where she stayed for the next 24 hours, with a supply of growers pellets and some water. I decided to call her *Holly*, and I'm pleased to say that it didn't take her long to settle in and start exploring the new run.

I quickly learned (despite what I'd read in the poultry books) that chickens don't necessarily return to their coop at night as if by clockwork! I had to catch *Holly* (not easy with the net!) and put her inside for the first few nights.

Routine established

Thankfully, though, she soon got the idea, and began putting herself to bed at the right time after about a week of encouragement from me. She was growing well, too, although took quite a while to learn about perching.

But I was still keen to get more birds, so I returned with my family to The Domestic Fowl Trust. This was a more successful visit. There were a number of hens for sale, including a Wellsummer that was close to PoL. My youngest stepson, Ben, spotted a Black Rock/Rhode Island Red hybrid of similar age, so that made three hens in all. Then my wife, Gail, had a complete change of heart. Having teased me all the way along about my new hobby ("Why on earth do you want to keep chickens?", "I'll have nothing to do with them!" and, "It's far cheaper just to buy the eggs!"), she spotted a bantam Wyandotte cockerel and was instantly smitten.

After another careful drive home I was eager to let our new chickens out into the run as soon as possible, so they could explore their new surroundings. But excitement rapidly turned to concern as the new, bigger chickens chased *Holly* all over the run, and pecked at her tail feathers.

So I acted fast and made a small enclosure for *Holly* inside the main run using some spare fencing. She was content with her own food and

Our Wyandotte bantam cockerel certainly rules the roost, being top of the pecking order

water, and this certainly solved the problem of how I was going to ensure that she ate growers pellets while the other three stuck to a layers ration.

The others had names by this stage, too; the Black Rock hybrid was called *Sam*. I called the brown Wellsummer *Speedy*, because she was impossible to catch (and still is). My wife chose *Prince* for the bantam cockerel, simply because of the way he strutted around the run.

Ever watchful

Every day, I keep a watchful eye on the chickens, and make sure their food and water is topped-up and the coop is clean. The wide-brimmed metal feeder, though more expensive than some alternatives, was well worth the extra money as the feed never gets wet. I clean the coop thoroughly once a week, and spray it with Poultry Shield.

After a month, I felt confident enough to let *Holly* out of her fenced-off area, initially during the daytime only. Since then she's gradually become integrated with the other chickens. However, the whole process has certainly made

me appreciate the real meaning of the term 'pecking order'.

Of course, little can adequately describe the joy of finding the first egg! It was still warm, but I wasn't sure which hen had laid it. I *think* it was *Sam*, but I still can't quite work out which of the lovely, large brown eggs is from which hen.

Foxes and rats have thankfully been absent so far, and the family cat happily co-exists with his new feathered friends.

I now realise that a two-metre fence is needed to keep the chickens in their enclosure; *Sam* was the first to escape and has since taught *Speedy* how to get over too. I've been firmly instructed not to clip their wings, but the 'escapees' have had a ball ripping up the old vegetables and our flowerbeds.

Sam is very friendly and easily handled. She has quickly learned where the corn is kept, and leads the others by running across the garden as soon as I approach the shed to get their afternoon feed! I have since discovered that chickens eat almost anything, including any *Rice Crispies* that my wife scatters on our patio.

I'm delighted that all the hens continue to voluntarily return to the coop in the evening, and also that *Holly* has finally learned to perch. I did initially consider buying an automatic door opener, or even retrofitting one after, but I enjoy the morning and evening walk up to the coop. I have also saved quite a sizeable potential cost.

No regrets

I certainly can't think of a single regret associated with the chickens. What's more, even with the benefit of hindsight, I wouldn't have done anything any differently. The hens add fun, colour and noise (we already had cockerels as neighbours) to the garden. I let them out for most of the day, though I shall have to think seriously about whether to fence in the chickens or the vegetables next year.

The lovely brown eggs are tasty, fresh and quickly eaten. Chickens are easy to own and take little time to keep a regular eye on. I would recommend home poultry keeping to anyone who has the space, time and enthusiasm.

A mixed bag

Mark Bowman reflects on the events of his first year with poultry

When we moved to our new home in North Cumbria, for the first time in our lives we had a home with a large garden, situated on the edge of a village. Our house is modern, detached and on a small estate. We overlook a field with views across the river to the Lakeland Fells in the far distance. It's an idyllic location with wildlife all around – thousands of Greylag geese over-winter in the fields, there are otters and kingfishers on the river, house martins nest under the eaves in the summer and deer and rabbits are seen in the field.

We quickly realised that there was a thin, rough strip of land between our garden fence and the farmer's field fence which wasn't used by anyone. During our first summer this strip of land became full of nettles and thistles and, when the thistledown seeded into our house and garden, we decided something had to be done!

Sowing the seeds

I made a gate through the garden fence into this 'jungle', and set about felling it with a scythe. Over the next year I chopped, mowed and threw down some grass seed. Slowly the land fell into some sort of repair. Our neighbours were encouraging as, the next summer, none of us were infested with quite so many thistle seeds! Nobody objected, so we decided to put this bonus garden to some use. We planted some fruit trees and bushes, built a few raised beds, had a ton or two of topsoil delivered and shoveled in barrowloads of horse muck from a nearby paddock. The following summer we reaped the rewards, enjoying our own new

*Above: **We compost everything we can, including all the waste from the hen house, to create a fantastic mulch for the fruit bushes***

potatoes, beans, courgettes and onions. Our neighbours benefited with the surplus too, so everyone was happy!

My wife Kate had long held the idea of keeping some chickens. This was partly born out of childhood memories of an aunt of hers who kept poultry in the cellar of her terraced house in the Lancashire town where she grew up. I was more skeptical, and didn't relish the prospect of upsetting our new neighbours with the sound of a crowing cockerel. One day, idling my time in a town bookshop, I spotted a book on poultry-keeping and bought it as a present for Kate (I thought she'd take a look at it and decide the whole enterprise would be too complicated, and the notion would be dropped). However, she kept looking at it and, then, I started too!

No cockerel was needed… interesting; perhaps we could get

some hens. The notion grew and a few months later we spotted a hen house for sale in the classified section of the local paper. A 'phone call later we found ourselves negotiating the purchase of a relatively new hut. It had been bought for a boy who'd wanted to keep chickens, but had never wanted to clean it out; he gradually lost interest. The house looked sound enough, although inside it was about six inches deep in dried-out hen muck. The asking price was £100 but, after a bit of haggling, we settling on £90, including delivery – a bargain! So, with it dismantled and loaded, we were on our way. An afternoon's power-washing and scrubbing proved that the basic structure was indeed sound and, after two coats of shed paint, it looked a chicken residence *par excellence*!

Birds for sale

The next job was to get some stock. The following week we were at our local pet food store and saw a notice in the 'For sale' corner advertising four Fallowfield hens. We'd no idea what they were but, keen to get started, we 'phoned and were soon on our way over the border to Gretna Green. Their owner, an elderly gentleman, gave us an impressive sales patter; these were the best hens he had ever owned – they just looked like brown hens to us – but he showed us their recent egg laying records, and said he'd throw in half a bag of feed and some grit just to get them started. Tentatively we asked the price – £10 the lot, so we bit off his hand!

He shooed the hens into their house, caught them and put them in a box for us. We transferred them to our car and were about to drive off and when he came rushing after us. "You'd better take these" he said, thrusting a box containing four eggs into Kate's hand, "They laid 'em today". One final piece of advice was to lock them in for an hour or two once we got them home, just so they'd know where they were to live, and we were on our way.

We did as instructed and, after a few hours, let them out making sure that there was some feed outside the door. We christened

Not bad for £90! Our secondhand hen house has room for 16 birds

them *Barbeque*, *Kiev*, *Korma* and *Nuggets*. Lo and behold they went back in the hen house before dark and, the next day we were rewarded with four eggs. Keeping hens seemed easy – a bit of feed, warm quarters and a supply of eggs... now't to it! Our neighbours were interested, and the occasional half-dozen surplus eggs passed over the garden fence were gratefully received.

One Saturday, early in September, we visited a poultry sale at a local auction mart. We'd gone

intending simply to have a look, but I ended up having to take Kate home before she started bidding! However, it was an interesting couple of hours, and we even met up with an old friend who gave us more useful advice.

Growing flock

In time the prospect of a few more hens began to seem appealing. We certainly had the room, as our poultry house was big enough for 16 birds and, after spotting an advert in the local paper for some multi-coloured bantams, we headed off to a remote farmhouse nestling in the dubious lands north of Hadrian's Wall but south of the Scottish border. Here we met a small, unwashed and elderly farmer with a large landing net.

"They're in this barn, but they might take a bit o' catching" he announced. We followed him in. There were dozens of birds hurtling and flapping about, which was made worse by his lunges and sweeps with the net. Not helped by his diminutive stature the capture of four bantams took some doing but, eventually, £10 changed hands and we were on our way home, accompanied by some advice to "clip their wings as they're a bit flighty".

We'd no experience of clipping

We built this smaller house and run to help with our breeding program although, at the time of writing, we've had no luck at all

wings but, after consulting the book, gave it a try. I hung on to each bird as Kate snipped away. The birds were then popped into the house and the door was locked. Our past experience with the Fallowfields suggested that a couple of hours to settle would suffice.

On opening the door later that day the bantams shot out like champagne corks and took to the air like ballistic missiles. Over the next few weeks going to the pub was a bit embarrassing as our bantams were causing havoc around the village, scratching up peoples' flower beds. One pub regular, Dave the Bus, had one living in his garden for several months and was delighted to see and feed it every day.

As the days shortened and food became scarce two of the bantams (*Blackie* and *Fluffy Whiskers*) began appearing at our feeding times and eventually we managed to catch them. This time we severely clipped their wings, sectioned off part of the hen house and kept them locked in for over a week. Upon their eventual release, they didn't wander too far, and came back in at dusk. The third bird remained in Dave's garden but, sadly, the fourth was never seen again.

Our hen-keeping was a source of great amusement to our family, and Kate's brother rang one day to see if I could go and collect a present he'd bought her. This turned out to be a pair of young Muscovy ducklings.

But he hadn't really got them himself; I had to go and collect them from a farm! And when I got there it turned out that I also had to catch them, aided by the farmer's elderly, asthmatic wife. We chased a gaggle of ducks around the farm yard, under tractors, over bales of hay and through muddy puddles until, eventually, we managed to catch two of them.

Ducks or drakes?

I propped the exhausted farmer's wife against a tractor wheel and thanked her very much. She assured me she'd be alright once she got her breath back, and that they were grand ducks. Boxed-up, I set off home, not sure whether I'd caught ducks or drakes. We hadn't really

Our mixed flock enjoy a free-range lifestyle, and seem to thrive on it

thought through what we'd do with them, and put them in with the chickens overnight. Our fence, which had contained the hens, proved no obstacle for the smaller ducks. They were quickly away and waddling off towards the river.

They did eventually come home, via the village duck pond and accompanied by an old Muscovy drake, and we fed them all. The ducks disappeared back to the pond but he stayed and is still with us. Over the next few months our ducks returned often, usually with other Muscovy ducks and drakes. Just this month one duck has paired-up with the old drake, and has started laying an egg each day in the hen house. What a bonus!

As winter turned to spring, one of our hens, *Barbeque*, became ill. Her droppings were watery, she lost weight and condition. Despite Kate's care and attention, she became very weak and unable to climb the small ramp into the hen

This is a Muscovy we call Julia Roberts, *after the black-and-white dress the actress once wore to an Oscar ceremony!*

house. I put her down. It was a great shame, she had a tremendous character; the most confident of our hens and, like the other three, a tremendous layer. But where there's a problem there's also an opportunity. Another poultry auction was taking place not far away so off we went and, after registering as buyers and collecting a catalogue, we set about inspecting the birds.

Amidst a great cacophony of crowing and clucking we wandered among the cages, checking the catalogue. Eventually we decided to bid for three Light Sussex point-of-lay pullets, which we got for £30 plus commission. They proved to be very easy to settle, and soon were in full production. Our Fallowfield hens had laid all winter so with the Light Sussex also laying as well, we were getting plenty of eggs. Cooked breakfasts were now weekday events instead of Sunday morning treats, and Kate's baking rate was increasing to keep up with supply – workmates and neighbours enjoyed the surplus!

Another auction saw us buying two more POL Marans pullets but, this time, we weren't careful enough. Closer inspection revealed that they had a mild infestation of scaly leg mite. But careful treatment with surgical spirit and Vaseline seems to have remedied the problem, and the brown eggs they now lay look and taste tremendous.

Shared passion

By now I was really getting the bug for keeping hens – it had become a hobby both of us could share. The bantams, one by one, became broody. 'Hastings', my fishing mate and fellow poultry keeper, told us we should pick them off the nest and throw them up into the air, this would cure them. However, given the bantams' past flying abilities, I decided to simply lift them off the nest at every opportunity, instead. It slowly worked, but *Blackie* eventually disappeared. After a few days she reappeared for food, but then promptly disappeared again; what was going on?

At about the same time, the bantam that had taken up residence with Dave the Bus started returning for breakfast each morning and, on one occasion, was heard to crow. A couple of weeks later *Blackie* reappeared with a tiny chick. Was Dave's bantam a cockerel?

I acquired an old rabbit hutch, knocked together a pen, caught the chick and its mother and we waited to see what this mystery offspring would be. To be honest, it didn't look like either of its 'parents', being a motley brown colour and, one morning, it suddenly flapped its wings, took off and disappeared. My conclusion was that it was a pheasant chick and that *Blackie*, being broody, had settled on a clutch of wild pheasant eggs and had managed to hatch one.

But these events fired our interest in breeding and, using my joinery skills, I set about building another hen house to accommodate further chicks but, with no cockerel, breeding our own was out of the question. One of the Light Sussex hens was now broody so against some of the advice given in *Practical Poultry*, I did an Internet search, found a reliable-looking website and sent off for half-a-dozen mixed hatching eggs. They arrived by return of post and the hen sat straight on them. For 20 days we waited in anticipation but, on the day before they were due to hatch, the hen got off and walked away. We didn't know what to do, she'd lost interest completely. We sat a broody bantam on them, but she wasn't interested either. Disappointed, I decided to crack one open – and found that it was totally addled. The smell was awful, and all the rest were the same.

Surprise find

After the disappointment of our first chicken hatching non-event, we settled down to a cup of tea only to be raised from our chairs by the doorbell ringing. Another neighbour had found a hen sitting on a nest. Was it ours? Dave's bantam/cockerel had disappeared a few weeks earlier and we'd assumed it'd gone back to him. I went to investigate only to find it was Dave's bird sitting on 11 eggs. Not a cockerel then! I caught her up and brought her and her eggs

Mr Muscovy meets our new Labrador pup for the first time!

home. We sat her in the new hen house, but she left the eggs. I cracked one open; it was addled and with no cockerel about clearly not fertile. We seem destined not to breed.

So it's summer now, most of the hens have moulted and this saw a drop in egg-laying. From getting seven or eight eggs a day, the total fell to just two or three. We don't know the age of the Fallowfield hens, they might be getting to the end of their days. One keeps laying soft-shelled eggs, but the Marans

Kate checks one of our layers for parasites

and Light Sussex are coming back into full laying condition, so the egg collection rate is beginning to improve. Kate continues to put her culinary skills to good use and, so far, has used the eggs to make pasta, mayonnaise, lemon curd, Scotch eggs and the usual cakes and custard.

We've got into a good system of cleaning, partly because it doesn't include me! The house floor is covered with wood shavings, and the nest boxes are filled with recycled, shredded paper. Kate picks up the muck every week and, once a month, she cleans the whole hen house thoroughly, spraying with Decimite to ward-off mites.

The muck, shavings and paper are composted, and used to make an excellent mulch for the fruit bushes. The hens seem content enough and have a free-range wooded area of about half an acre to wander and scratch about in. We feed them poultry mash in the morning and some organic corn in the evening.

And so our first year of poultry-keeping drew to a close. We'd enjoyed the experience and had a lot of laughs as well as some disappointments. We probably made lots of mistakes, but are keen to continue; we're even planning to buy a cockerel!

Teacher's pets

Chris Graham meets Rachel Johnson – a keeper new to the hobby who has gone about things the right way and is loving every minute of it!

Following a move to the site of an old plant nursery nestling in a picturesque, rural East Sussex valley – complete with its own artesian well – Rachel Johnson finally had the opportunity to get some hens. But with her job as an art teacher at a local school, a new house build to oversee with husband Peter, plus the constant desire to develop her ability as an artist in her own right (Rachel Widdows M.A.), spare time for new hobbies was always going to be at a premium.

Rachel's also a very enthusiastic rabbit keeper and, with close links to The Kit Wilson Trust – a local pet rescue organisation – takes in rabbits of all sorts; be they victims of cruelty, neglect, illness or simply old age. But owning chickens has been a long-held ambition for her. "My husband's grandmother raised chickens commercially, and my father's aunt kept Leghorns on a farm. The sound of cockerels crowing is one of the sounds of my childhood, so there's definitely a sentimental link there," she explains.

"But I really started wanting some hens of my own about two or three years ago, and that's when I picked up my first copy of *Practical Poultry*. It was the magazine that first introduced me to the idea of battery hen rescue, and the existence of the Battery Hen Welfare Trust.

"Initially I'd thought about keeping rare breeds, and was keen on the Scots Grey. But I was so struck by the BHWT's work that I decided that their's was the way forward for me. Animal welfare is a key issue

The hens enjoy a free-range lifestyle, and their interest in all things domestic has blossomed!

for me and the ethos behind the BHWT simply struck a chord."

Fools rush in...

Unlike many beginners, Rachel didn't rush into her new hobby, and actually bought her first poultry ark about two years before getting a single bird! In fact, the ark was pressed into service as a rabbit house, although it wasn't entirely appropriate for this. As things turned out, it hasn't proved particularly practical for the hens

Rachel was keen to have a 'walk-in' hen house; much easier to live with in all respects

either. Rachel explained, "It quickly became obvious to me that what chickens really need is space, and plenty of it. The ark is just too restrictive although it has been used a few times as an isolation unit, but that's about it.

"My original five hens came from a BHWT regional co-ordinator in Sussex. They were taken from a group of birds that had been held back after a previous rescue, because they were too weak to be re-homed at that stage. I went to pick them up last January, and paid 50p each for them (as a donation). The co-ordinator, Sarah, was a lovely girl who'd actually knitted 'jumpers' for use by those rescued birds that were particularly lacking in feathers." Rachel appreciates that she's still new to poultry keeping, but she loves research and reading, and already has a mini reference library focussed on chickens.

Thanks to the preparation done before getting the hens, Rachel was completely ready for them, and knew just what to expect. "All five had mites, were pretty 'wormy' and anaemic when they arrived," she says "But I was ready for this thanks to what I'd read. I'd also taken plenty of advice from friends, and Tom, a very knowledgeable man at Windmill Feeds, my local feed merchants; he's an absolute mine of information.

"I'd intended to wait until the girls were fully-feathered before giving them names, but we couldn't hold out and started calling them things like 'limper', 'scrawny' and 'dinosaur' which, I'm afraid, sort of stuck. Not very flattering, I know – particularly as I'd wanted to give them pretty, old-fashioned names like Maude and Jemima. Since then, though, at least 'dinosaur' has been shortened to 'dina', which is marginally better!"

Settling-in

As soon as it became apparent that the ark was going to be too small for the five hens, Rachel set about converting a 7x7' shed that had previously been used as rabbit accommodation.

"I was keen to have a poultry house that provided plenty of space for the birds, but was also big enough for me to walk into," she explains. "We have a large polytunnel here which I hope to convert using a kit that includes a new, heat-deflecting plastic sheeting and mesh and wooden panels at the side for ventilation. The tunnel measures 19x8m, so I hope to get several houses inside it, each with a good run area attached."

For the time being, though, the birds revel in an essentially free-range lifestyle, being shut-up only when Rachel and Peter are both out. "I've added a secure and covered run to the main poultry house; I built this myself over the Easter holidays this year, using leftover wood and wire from my rabbit enclosure. This provides an additional area of about 10x12ft that's secure and dry for the birds to use while we're away."

Rachel recalls that the eggs were quite poor early on, often being laid with no shell at all, or just a very thin one. However, as the birds have recovered, gained plumage and settled in, so the egg quality has improved dramatically. "During the first few weeks of ownership I noticed that some of the eggs were being eaten, which was obviously a worry because I knew it could become a serious and habitual vice," she recalls. "Thankfully, though, it just stopped once they'd all settled down; I'm sure the spacious environment and the improvement in their quality of life played a big part in this."

Flushed with success, the decision was taken to rescue another five birds, and these came via the same route. The newcomers were part of a giant BHWT and Brighton Animal Action rescue, which saw 13,500 birds saved in one swoop. The whole experience has certainly altered Rachel's attitude towards ex-battery hens, as she explains. "I suppose, like many other people, my perception of rescued birds was that they'd be timid, sad creatures, lacking in confidence. But my short time with these birds has shattered this illusion, which couldn't have been further from the truth. My birds are friendly and engaging characters who are more than happy to be handled. They have a wonderful curiosity about everything that's going on, and display a truly fantastic zest for life."

This large polytunnel will eventually be cleared, re-covered with agricultural-grade, heat-deflecting plastic, and used to house the poultry

Food for thought

"I began feeding with layers pellets, but these weren't 100% successful with all the girls, so I switched to mash. Once a week I turn this into a sort of porridge

Feather re-growth has taken its time, but the birds' return to health has gone hand in hand with a significant improvement in egg quality

using water, with added Poultry Spice, cod liver oil and pro-biotic yoghurt! They all seem to prefer it, so I've fed it ever since.

"I try to resist feeding them too many kitchen scraps because I've read that these can fill the crops which then stops the birds eating their primary layers feed. All the hens are laying, so I'm very conscious that the quality of their diet needs to be maintained. I leave food available *ad hoc*, and place it in the house, in the run and nearby, outside. I started doing this initially because I was concerned about the risk of bullying, and wanted food available in enough separate places to ensure that all birds got their fair share.

"I've just started using apple cider vinegar as an additional supplement in the drinking water. I add this for a few days at a time, then give them a break from it and, so far, everything seems fine and they're all drinking perfectly normally, which is great. I've also just read about the use of garlic, but I haven't begun with this yet. I'm slightly concerned about the tainting issue and certainly wouldn't want to dissuade the birds from drinking in any way."

floor is covered with a mixture of sand and gravel, although this isn't ideal. I'm thinking of adding a layer of woodchip on top which will be easier to change on a regular basis. I really should take the plunge and adopt a deep litter system in there, but I do worry about the hygiene implications of that approach."

Final solutions

Of course, Rachel's caring, sensitive attitude makes things tricky when hard decisions have to be taken. She admits that it could be a bit of a problem, saying: "I don't quite know what's going to happen when the birds reach the end of the line. I think that Peter would be able to deal with them if they were suffering, but I know that I couldn't do that. I would resort to the vet if any of the hens were suffering."

However, on a happier note, it's clear from talking to her that Rachel derives a tremendous amount of satisfaction and pleasure from her chickens. Keeping them is evidently a pure joy, and a delight that's made all the sweeter in the knowledge that the birds she owns have been saved from a most untimely end. The idea of progressing towards rare breed poultry appeals to her as well, with the conservation and preservation aspects attached to that being uppermost in her mind.

Wherever the hobby leads her, though, it's obvious that any birds lucky enough to end up in her care will be fortunate creatures indeed. •

Here's the run that Rachel built over the Easter holiday! Note the wire mesh extension out along the ground, as an anti-predator measure

Next I asked Rachel how her birds had faired, healthwise. "From my experience with poorly rabbits I'm very aware of the importance of constant monitoring and regular handling. Rabbits are very susceptible to stress, and I know chickens are too. It can be a big problem that becomes very debilitating, making the birds far more susceptible to any sort of disease they may encounter. The whole re-homing experience tends to be a stressful one for ex-battery hens, so extra care is needed.

"I'm very pro-active with handling and inspecting my birds on a regular basis and, in this way, I'm able to monitor their overall condition and notice any changes. Frequent observation is a key factor too. It's important to be aware of how well each of your birds is eating and drinking, and you simply can't do that if you don't spend

enough time with them. Once again, like rabbits, chickens are very good at disguising any health problems they may have, so that when they finally do start to show outward symptoms, their overall condition is usually quite serious.

"So far, I've been lucky, and my birds haven't suffered any serious problems at all. I'd certainly be very quick to call in the vet at the first sign of anything that I didn't think I could handle. I'm fairly fastidious about general hygiene and cleanliness which, again, comes from my experience with rabbits. Both they and chickens are very prone to upper respiratory and eye problems, so clean and dust-free conditions inside their houses are vital.

"For this reason I change the house bedding material on a daily basis, and never use anything other than softwood shavings. The run

And so to bed...

Chicken fun!

Erick Woods explains how he and his wife Linda have created one of the most unusual poultry environments you're likely to see anywhere!

Above: Erick and Linda Woods set out to provide their birds with added interest in the run, and have certainly achieved this so far

For a great many of us, satisfying our pet's essential needs for proper care simply isn't enough. No matter what their size, shape or intellectual prowess, we often go above and beyond what would seem to be perfectly adequate, striving to extend some measure of 'royal treatment' to them. Special ways of expressing our gratitude, in return for the pleasure, utility and companionship they provide.

We firmly believe that poultry are more than worthy of such adoration and luxury. Chickens create laughter, love and beauty in our lives; they captivate our imaginations. On a one-acre slice of rural heaven at our home in northern California, our hens have given us an abundance of joy. The unmatched flavour of their fresh eggs, the rainbow of feathers produced for our crafts, the fabulous fertiliser for our garden, and the countless hours of pleasure gained from observing their many wacky antics are among the precious benefits we enjoy.

So, in return for all these wonderful favours, we've constructed some super-deluxe accommodation for our feathered friends, known affectionately these days as the 'Prancing Poultry Resort' – a name inspired by *Lord of the Rings*.

Limited experience

In fact, our chicken cottage/resort project – which began in earnest early in 2005 – represents the sum total of Linda's experience with keeping poultry of any kind. Fortunately, from the outset she was open and cautiously eager to give the cluckers a try, provided a couple of important provisos were observed. It was agreed that most of the care and cleaning duties would be my responsibility and, secondly, that we wouldn't keep roosters. So I assured Linda that top-notch poultry management was guaranteed, and promised she would grow to love these creatures, as I have.

As for me, well, I was introduced to chickens eight years ago, in a rather serendipitous way by a friend named Duane. What began one day as a casual conversation at work ended with Duane providing me with chapter and verse on his poultry hobby – the chicks he reared, the variety of exotic breeds he kept and the delicious eggs they laid. I was hooked and, following a visit to meet his flamboyant flock, I decided I wanted to keep chickens too.

By the following spring, I'd designed and built my first hen house (complete with fully-enclosed run) and was anxiously awaiting a call from the local postal depot with the news that my chicks had arrived and were ready for collection. The first coop was a small structure – roughly 8'x3', and only three feet or so high – so not a walk-in affair by any means. It had a mesh base, and double-layered side doors on each end to aid airflow and temperature control. Inside I fitted an array of perches at various heights, plus several nest boxes.

The coop was mounted on stilts, which kept it about 18in above ground, providing additional areas

External nest boxes ease the collection of eggs. The house has multiple entry and exit points for the birds

of shade for relaxation during hot weather. The attached run measured 16'x30', and was fully enclosed and electrified to discourage the other chicken lovers (the raccoons, skunks, foxes and hawks we get in our neck of the woods). All-in-all, the entire set-up constituted decent digs for the dozen chickens.

New house

Then, a move to Washington State yielded new batches of chickens and a new coop. This time the

structure was built from plans published in a great book called *Poultry House Construction*, by Gold Cockerel Series publishing. This was a larger, stand-alone house; about 8'x5', and was just about big enough to get inside for cleaning purposes. The extremely harsh winters in eastern Washington necessitated the need for artificial heat, provided by infrared lamps, and a water de-icer.

The chickens coexisted quite happily with two cute-as-could-be pygmy goats, sharing a fenced (though not predator-proof) area of about an acre. Life for these northern latitude ladies went swimmingly until, that is, the raccoons stumbled upon them. A nightly feast ensued and the carnage was horrible! In spite of several attempts at discouraging the marauding intruders (the charming goats had no deterrent effect whatsoever), the chicken population dwindled rapidly. In no time at all the original 20 were reduced to just four lucky survivors, who were hurriedly carted-off to another place where they could expect a more promising fate. Then, a few more life changes conspired to bring me back, full-circle, to California and the town where I enjoyed my first batch of chickens.

A combination of carpentry and electrical skills, passed along and nourished by my father, were major

Linda is relatively new to poultry keeping, but now embraces the whole project with the same enthusiasm and drive as Erick

The contentedness of the hens enjoying life in the Californian Prancing Poultry project means that even the youngest human visitor is always made welcome

Safety first

The attached run currently measures 24'x50', and is topped with bird netting intended to deter hawks from taking our little bantams, and prevents the chickens from getting out. However, this netting has proved very fragile, and also seems to have played a part in the unfortunate death of at least one chicken. Consequently, its replacement is high on the list of resort improvements scheduled for this coming year. A 'shock wire' encircles the entire run (apart from the gate) and has been brilliant at keeping out all manner of ground threats. The chickens do a fair amount of roosting on the large, dead apple tree branch, which rests on one end of the run. They also indulge in an invigorating bath in their dusting box, filled with equal quantities of fine earth and sand.

Having our appetite whetted with the success of the Prancing Poultry, and knowing that our hens enjoyed the many cottage levels, we felt sure they'd fancy an additional structure attached to the cottage itself, featuring an array of ramps and walkways. These would be accessible from different locations, and would also allow entry into and out of the cottage. Thus the Jungle Gym idea was hatched and, since its completion last summer, it's been an immensely popular and often-used addition to the resort.

The Woods' Californian hens enjoy plenty of space, a good, mixed diet and lots of stimulation. The large run is kept secure by electrification

MEET THE MENAGERIE

The breeds currently enjoying life at the Prancing Poultry resort include: Blue Andalusian, Silver pencilled Hamburgh, Delaware, White Rock, Black Jersey Giant, Salmon Faverolles, Red Cochin bantams, Black Silkie, Buff Orpington, Cornish and Ameraucana (we just love those blue-green eggs).

New breeds on the horizon include: Belgian Millefleur and Porcelaine bantams, Old English Red Game, Araucana, Silver Sebrights, plus large fowl versions of Araucana, Speckled Sussex, White Orpington, Sultan, Buff Brahma, Cuckoo Marans, Lakenvelders, Buttercups, Fayoumi, Barred Rock, Red Cap, Golden Campine, Poland, Phoenix and, last but not least, Silver Grey Dorking.

Finally, as you may have already guessed, every last one of our chickens has a name!

factors in influencing my present-day aim of creating first-class hen houses. The current Prancing Poultry Resort project consists of a coop (or cottage, as we like to call it) that's eight feet square, and eight feet tall. It has a standard wooden frame and is clad with OSB sheeting. The floor is built similarly, with two coats of paint for protection and insulation for a bit of sound-deadening. The roof is a simple A-frame type affair, with composite shingles. A large person-sized door, with a chicken-size opening, leads inside.

Our hens actually have a few ways in and out of this dwelling, including a balcony and Jungle Gym access. The nest boxes extend out from the cottage, allowing for easy egg access. Exterior accoutrements include a solar-powered porch light, rain awnings, and a stern reminder of their nightly guild meetings (presumably to discuss the day's activities!). As chickens readily take to climbing and roosting at various heights, we built them a series of ramps and walkways within the cottage, which serve to both increase the total usable space of an already sizable structure, while allowing easy access to nest boxes and roosts at a good many different levels.

I built the Jungle Gym using 2"x4" and 1"x2" wood framing, and OSB sheeting. It features three level platforms plus three ramps, each presenting a 15° incline, with steps at six-inch intervals. A ribbon-cutting ceremony was held for the grand opening, and all those in attendance had a splendid time. We now get a fantastic amount of pleasure

Don't be late!

The interior of the main poultry house is large enough to allow modifications for extra interest too – ramps, multiple perches and walkways ensure plenty to do

take the welfare of our birds as a laughing matter. Our philosophy is that proper care begins with maintaining clean conditions throughout the birds' living environment (particularly true for poultry confined to a limited area). This doesn't mean sterile, germ-free living conditions (an aim neither possible nor desirable), but it does demand the diligent, periodic removal of accumulated droppings and detritus. We're also methodical about treating cleaned surfaces, feeders and drinkers with a proper disinfectant (we use 70% alcohol mixed with a 1:10 bleach solution).

The poultry house bedding is regularly changed too, on a monthly basis. We prefer pine shavings rather than straw, as it tends to be a cleaner, drier material overall, while also lending a pleasant scent to the 'cottage'. To aid parasite control, we use a combination of a poultry protector spray in the nest boxes, mite strips hung in their entryways, and a mite powder liberally sprinkled in the birds' dust-bathing box.

Our hens enjoy a year-round supply of organic 'laying crumbles' (16% protein), supplemented with a mixed buffet of organic scratch and kitchen scraps (whole grain bread, grapes, melons and lettuce are their favourite delicacies). They also get a weekly treat of honey-sweetened cooked oatmeal. Clean, fresh water is ever-present (thankfully, without the need for de-icers here in temperate California), as are an oyster shell calcium supplement, and granite grit for their grinding gizzards.

Overall, it's been enormously satisfying to share our creation with family and friends. The Prancing Poultry resort has hosted many guests of all ages (the youngsters invariably adopt the cottage as their own play house!). What's more, everyone who's visited has given our efforts the thumbs-up. Even more importantly, though, the chickens seem to like it too, judging by their contented behaviour and good health. I'd certainly recommend the sort of additions we've created to anyone who wants to spice-up everyday life for their birds.

After all, there's no telling where your ideas may lead you! •

Erick believes high welfare standards are key to good poultry keeping. House litter is never allowed to become damp or dirty

from watching our birds cruising all over the Jungle Gym; from ground level, all the way up into their cottage and back!

Future plans

However, we're not sitting on our laurels and have plenty more ideas for developing our fledgling resort further. These include a Jungle Gym mezzanine with more nest boxes, a run extension (hosting a second multi-level coop, tentatively named 'Egg Manor', cobblestone pathways throughout the resort grounds, a rolling mesh platform to allow for continuous grazing of fresh range (currently, the green goodies are brought to our girls as mown grass and weeds), additional ramps and walkways, solar path lights and a bench designed in castle motif.

However, despite all the fun and games involved in these ideas, I'd like to stress that we certainly don't

Allow new birds plenty of time to settle inside after the move. Also be aware of the disease risk if mixing with an existing flock

Happy hybrids

Terry Beebe takes a look at the ups and downs of living with ex-battery hens

Battery hens live in a very controlled environment, so bringing them into a domestic one needs to be handled with care

I've watched with interest as the Battery Hen Welfare Trust has established itself in the UK (www.thehenshouse.co.uk). The work this charity does is quite amazing and, although there's been a bit of criticism from some quarters, I believe the whole project has helped significantly to generate an interest in poultry among a whole sector of the population who might otherwise never have become involved.

It's really heart-warming to see the concern that an ever-increasing number of people have for the plight of ex-battery birds and, although those rescued only count for a tiny percentage of the national commercial flock, I believe it's the effort and commitment to save as many as possible that counts.

Think first

However, it's also very important that new owners don't get carried away with the euphoria of the whole experience. It can be all too easy to get drawn into the battery hen rescue idea on a wave of good intention, and overlook some of the more practical considerations involved. So here I'll run through some of the basics relating specifically to the health and welfare of these birds, post-rescue.

The first thing to appreciate is that these hybrid hens are specialist creatures that have been developed and bred for a specific purpose. From the day they are hatched to the point they are slaughtered, they are fed and watered automatically. They are also treated with various antibiotics, and vaccinated against a wide range of poultry diseases, to ensure they remain as healthy and productive as possible.

However, this vaccination program in itself can pose a problem if rescued hens are mixed in with an existing flock of unvaccinated chickens. This is because the battery hens will, in most cases, be carrying low levels of the diseases against which they have been vaccinated. For this reason they are known as 'carriers' and they can present a health risk to other domestically-reared fowl.

Consequently, it's very important to keep a close eye on the general health of all your birds following the introduction of rescued hens. You should remain vigilant for a few weeks at least, until you're sure that all is well. If you don't have any other birds then, of course, this problem won't arise. However, don't ever let this disease risk put you off having rescued birds; all problems can easily be overcome.

Getting started

Organisations like the BHWT take great care to ensure that the rescued birds it distributes to new owners are in good condition; those which are 'under the weather' are retained at the rescue centre, and allowed to convalesce. But this doesn't mean that your new birds can instantly be put outside to fend for themselves, though. Remember that most battery hens will have led extremely 'sheltered' lives, never

Given adequate time, care and attention, ex-battery hens make ideal pets for the novice keeper

having seen daylight, eaten off the ground or scratched around in the earth for grubs. So the big wide world is a daunting and potentially frightening prospect, and newly-rescued hens must be eased into their new surroundings with care and consideration.

Don't expect new birds to adjust quickly either. I've known cases where hens put into a shed that has good light, plenty of space and an open pop hole haven't dared venture outside for up to a week. In some instances we've actually resorted to lifting them out by hand, but always find that, once out, they really enjoy the freedom they discover.

Another aspect which many new owners find surprising is how bad the birds can look. Lots of new owners are shocked by the apparently poor condition of the hens they get. Most will have suffered from feather pecking and general feather loss and, in fact, some will appear to be almost bald. Despite this, the feathers will all grow back again. With the right care and attention, they'll soon look quite normal and as attractive as ever!

The actual feather replacement does take time – in some cases up to six weeks. In my experience, one of the best ways to help the birds

through this stressful time is to add vitamins to their diet. Their bodies are working hard to replace the lost feathers, and this requires plenty of calcium and extra energy. Vitamins are easy and cheap to buy, and should form an essential part of your poultry first-aid kit. There are several well-known treatments available, including Poultry Spice and Battles Poultry Drink. Your choice is governed essentially by whether you want to add the treatment to the birds' feed or their drinking water.

Another aspect of the birds' appearance which may bother the new keeper is that some of them may well have had their beaks trimmed. In certain cases they will have been 'de-beaked' – the upper beak is cut shorter then the lower one to prevent feather pecking and egg eating. Although this may look odd, it has little effect on a bird's ability to eat and drink. Also, given time, the beaks will often re-grow.

Dealing with newly-acquired, ex-battery hens is as much about good old-fashioned common sense as looking after any other sort of poultry. Just don't rush things – give them time to settle, ensure they have clean, well-ventilated and dry housing, and don't turn part-feathered birds out if the weather is cold. Allow them to establish themselves happily and these hens will reward you with a good supply of tasty eggs for breakfast!

Feeding

I'm also asked often about how best to feed ex-battery birds. Well, these birds, being used to conveyer belt-supplied feed and nipple-type drinkers, often don't recognise the sort of feeders and drinkers that most backyard keepers use. So I suggest it's sensible to shake a little feed on to the floor once they are in the house, and gently spill a little water to give them the idea of where the food and water is. Don't soak the floor, or scatter too much food, as this will attract other visitors, such as rats and mice.

Personally I use layers pellets, but a good quality mash will be OK too. You can also add a little wheat, but only as a treat. If you want eggs, then feed the birds what they need to produce these for you. Stick to a professional, balanced feed product, and add feed treats such as cabbage, fresh fruit, mixed corn and bread (small amounts) in sensible quantities only. My own birds love apples, which are another great dietary supplement.

Water is easy to supply, and there are a large number of properly designed drinkers on the market. Bowls can be used, although they tend to get polluted by droppings and litter from the floor, so are more of an effort to keep clean. A constant supply of fresh, clean drinking water is absolutely essential for all poultry.

Try to cover drinkers and feeders if you can and, ideally, keep the feeder in the hen house. This will help prevent rodents and wild birds helping themselves, reducing the risks of disease and wastage. It also encourages the birds to return in the evening for their last feed of the day.

Precious plants?

Once the birds are settled into their new surroundings, it won't take long for them to become very tame. This is what most people want from these birds – pets and egg layers!

One word of warning, though. If you are a keen gardener, or if you already have an ornamental garden, then you must think about

Many new owners are still shocked by how down-at-heel rescued hens look, but the birds can soon be made to look healthy again

protecting the precious areas from the hens with some form of fencing. All breeds of poultry dig, and ex-battery hybrids are no exception. Given the chance, these hens clear an area of all forms of plant life in a very short space of time. They are just like little JCBs on legs!

The birds will quickly establish a favourite patch of soil where they will take a dust bath – the natural way they treat themselves against parasites. This can be anything up to two feet across, and will be in an area where the soil is very dry and fine. Dust-bathing is a very important activity for hens but, even if you see them doing it regularly, you'll still need to keep a close watch on their condition for yourself. Handle them all regularly to inspect for signs of the most common parasites (lice and mites). It's sensible to give them all a good shake of anti-louse powder just to be on the safe side.

Battery hens are pushed to the limit when 'in service', so don't expect 300+ eggs a season from rescued birds

While on the subject of parasites, it's also good practice to worm your birds on a regular basis. The move to a new environment may promote this problem and, if you're in any doubt, contact your local vet.

Hybrids, such as the ISA Brown (this is a trade name for a battery hen, although the name does change subject to the breeder or supplier) are actually a cross between a Rhode Island Red and a Light Sussex. They are fantastic layers and are among the easiest of all poultry breeds to keep and manage. They are what's classed as 'low maintenance', although you shouldn't imagine for a minute that this means they don't actually need to be looked after, because they certainly do. But, unlike some of the speciality pure breeds, they don't have any specific husbandry needs that make them more difficult for the novice keeper to cope with.

The same rules apply to these birds as for all poultry – cleanliness and good quality feed are essential. General checking for fleas, red mite and a regular worming should be just about all that's required to keep both you and the birds happy.

Finally, always remember where the birds have come from, and that they will have been laying heavily for up to 18 months or so. Give them a rest and bear in mind that although the production may not be as plentiful as it once was, these birds are well worth the effort. •

Beginner's luck

Tim Harper's introduction to poultry keeping has been far from smooth, but he has realised a boyhood dream of raising his own birds

Gold and silver Dutch chicks, with their 'Cleopatra' make-up!

Tim has enjoyed mixed success with ducks

When I was six years old my school teacher announced to the class that we were to start a new project, and that it was to be about animals that hatched from eggs. So, over the coming weeks, we learnt about snakes and snails and, of course, chickens.

An incubator was installed in the corner of the classroom to help with our investigations, and a dozen large, brown eggs were placed promisingly inside. Once a week our teacher would assure us that the eggs were indeed turning into chicks, and each member of the class would file past the incubator and peer longingly inside; desperate to be the first to see a chick.

On the third Monday, as the class filed into to the room, our teacher told us we had to be very quiet as the eggs had hatched. An instant hush descended over the room and this time, as we filed past the incubator, we looked down to see a clutch of fluffy, yellow chicks.

However, that was the last we saw of those birds, but the teacher assured us that they had gone to live in a good home. But, even at that age, I felt robbed. So I promised myself that, one day, I'd hatch my own chicks and watch them grow.

Now, fast-forward 12 years and you find me as an 18-year-old, still as keen on animals as I was at Primary school, and equally determined to put that long-held poultry plan into action.

First steps

In the end, it proved surprisingly easy to get started. A quick search on the internet turned-up a poultry supplier nearby and, within a few days, I was the proud owner of a small incubator and brooder. Then, the following weekend I visited a country fair, and bought some hatching eggs. Having limited space and living on a housing estate, I opted for Dutch bantams, and got half-a-dozen eggs (three gold and three silver), then supplemented these with six Indian runner duck eggs.

All were installed in the incubator and I soon began a repeat of the childhood process of regular checking but, this time, four times a day to turn the eggs, rather than just the once. Three weeks later my efforts were rewarded by the arrival of a single silver and two gold Dutch chicks – each was little bigger than a large bumble bee, and wore dark eyeliner around their eyes in the style of Cleopatra! They were followed, a week later, by a single duckling that looked like a rather tall Mallard.

In a few short days the fluff began to disappear and, as feathers started to appear, so did each of the birds' characters. The two gold chicks both treated me with the sort of adulation teenage girls normally reserve for members of a boy band, and would perch happily on my shoulder like tiny parrots. I decided to name them *Gerty* and *Miriam*. The silver chick was much more confident and, while he enjoyed a tummy tickle, treated me with a suspicion which lead me to believe he was a male bird, so I named him *Archie*. Cockerels had never been part of the plan, but I've always been known for my sentimental streak. Consequently, I couldn't bring myself to part with *Archie*, and decided to keep my trio intact.

However, although I'd achieved my dream of hatching my own birds, I'd also created something of a nightmare, in the form of *Daisy the duck*! If the hens liked me, *Daisy* positively worshipped the hens, and would quack out a loud distress call the instant they disappeared from sight. Also, despite the name, '*Daisy*' turned out to be a male bird. The consequent size difference worried me too. *Daisy*, in his enthusiasm for his poultry pals, would frequently send them skidding across the ground in his eagerness to greet them.

More birds

To my mind there was only one solution; I dusted-down the incubator and prepared it for a second batch of eggs. I'd planned to buy them at another country fair, but happened to pop into the local butchers the day before, and got talking about my avian chums. The butcher told me he had a batch of duck eggs which had only just been delivered. He assured me that they were Indian Runners, so I bought half-a-dozen to sample

Tim is careful to keep bird numbers closely in check to avoid overcrowding

what I'd soon have a bountiful supply of, hopefully! But my mind has never really worked the same way as everyone else's and, somewhere between the shop and home, I had convinced myself that it would be worth trying these new eggs in the incubator.

Somewhat surprisingly, my impulsiveness was rewarded by a single chick which, when it hatched, was quite possibly the cutest thing I'd ever seen. It really was the original 'chocolate box kid', with its large, orange beak and plenty of yellow fluff. However, the one thing it wasn't was an Indian Runner! I decided to name the new

Tim's time with poultry so far has run far from smoothly, but he's certainly making progress

arrival '*Dylis*', and she grew at the most incredible rate; so much so that visiting friends were convinced that I was fattening a goose for Christmas lunch! Within six weeks *Dylis* was bigger than both my dogs, and dwarfed *Daisy* too.

In fact, *Daisy* took one look at *Dylis* and ran the other way, and kept running in the opposite direction for the best part of a month. During this period, what had once been a respectable lawn began to disappear under a never-ending sea of duck poo. *Dylis* was the proud possessor of a very, very regular bowel movement.

Then, one night, *Daisy* changed his mind about *Dylis* and, forgetting all about his poultry pals, fell hopelessly in love with the buxom beauty. At the same time *Daisy* begun to fear my intentions towards his beloved and, from that day on, I would be attacked as soon as I stumbled into sight. At first I found it all rather amusing but, with time, *Daisy*'s paranoia about my evil intent increased, and so did the strength of his attacks.

Without wishing to dwell on the subject too much, I must mention again here *Dylis*' prestigious bowel performance. Those of you who've never had to run across a lawn liberally sprinkled with the contents of a healthy duck's bowel won't appreciate just how slippery it can be. Black ice has nothing on it and,

Space is tight in the Harper household!

after a few weeks of landing flat on my back in the aforementioned mess, then being set upon by a vigilante duck, I decided that something had to change. *Dylis* and *Daisy* had reached the end of the line.

One last peck

Fortunately I managed to find them both a secure home, complete with a large pond. It seemed ideal and, as I released the pair with a heavy heart, *Daisy* turned, looked me up and down, delivered a parting jab just below the knee, and was gone. The departure of these two made for a pretty quiet winter and, by the time Spring arrived, I was reaching for the incubator once again.

This time I took two eggs each from *Gerty* and *Miriam*, and popped them into the machine. Just under three weeks later, three chicks hatched – each a carbon copy of their mother. I named them *April*, *May* and *June*. Sadly, after just a few days, *May* became ill and died shortly afterwards. But *April*

and *June* thrived and, in due course, grew into beautiful silver hens.

The egg supply from Gerty and Miriam had far exceeded my expectations, although the eggs themselves were small. So, as the duck pen was now empty, I thought I might try a few larger hens. The birds would still need to be bantams as space is very short, plus there was the noise aspect to consider as well.

I'm definitely a supporter of rare breeds, so settled on the Nankin. This is a beautiful breed, cloaked in a thick, rich red plumage; they are solid-looking little birds too. I managed to get in touch with a specialist breeder and ordered six hatching eggs. When the time came for the birds to hatch, the first chick pipped its shell then died. The second was clearly deformed and died within minutes of hatching, but the third and final one to emerge seemed normal.

However, as the tiny yellow chick dried and started trying to stand, it became clear there was

something wrong with this one as well. A quick internet search suggested that the problem might be splayed legs, and the general thinking was that it should be destroyed. However, I also read about leg splinting as a possible solution and, seeing as the hatch had been so disappointing, and considering that this chick looked generally strong, I decided to give it a go.

Splinting the leg of a tiny, day-old chick certainly isn't as easy as it sounds. But, after several attempts and a good deal of swearing, the chick had both legs splinted with chopped-down cocktail sticks and plaster. At first it stumbled around like a drunk, but quickly got the hang of walking, albeit in the style of a pirate! After ten days I removed the plasters, and was delighted to find that the chick was able to walk normally. From this point on the it thrived, but it soon became clear that I'd hatched a second cockerel. But having fought so hard to keep the little fella alive, I had no intention of culling or

Nankin bantams are a particular interest, despite being a challenging bird to breed

selling him, and he was named *Ted*, and moved in to the old duck house. I didn't want him to live alone, so ordered three point-of-lay Nankin hens from the breeder.

When the hens arrived it soon became clear that I'd been spoilt with my easy-to-handle, friendly hens. Each of the Nankins was petrified of me; two of them screamed in terror whenever my hand appeared. The third simply attacked whenever I got close. So the latter was christened *Nasty Nancy* and the other two *Emily* and *Nelly*.

Troubled times

Then, barely a week after the new hens had arrived, more trouble struck. *Ted* went very quiet, lost his appetite and died. The guilt I felt when this happened was immense. After struggling so hard to get him walking and keep him alive, I'd then stupidly introduced him to three unquarantined birds, which had killed him.

Within a week of *Ted*'s death, *Nancy* went lame and, as her condition didn't improve, I took her to the vet. This was the first time I'd been able to handle her properly, and I could see that she was riddled with lice, and quite underweight. The vet diagnosed Marek's disease; a highly contagious illness that put all my birds at risk. Fortunately, none of my originals developed symptoms, but both *Nelly* and *Emily* died within three months of arriving.

When I contacted the breeder to inform her that she was selling sickly birds with a highly infectious disease, she disputed the diagnosis but did admit that Nankins are a sickly breed. Her explanation was that, as the gene pool for the breed is so small, you can't avoid inbreeding, which results in sickly birds. She also claimed that out-crossing to a different breed would dilute the gene pool. So, in effect, she's preserving a gene pool but in doing so, destroying a breed. As the vet who treated my birds put it: "It's no wonder it's a rare breed."

While I understand that birds do get sick, and that sometimes these things can't be helped, I will certainly be very careful about buying-in birds in the future. My first two years of poultry keeping have provided many ups and unfortunately a few downs. But even in the midst of the 'Nankin crisis', I knew it would not be long before I was reaching for my incubator again. Thankfully, I can report that the buzz I feel from watching the miracle of new life is as strong now as it was when I was six years old!

One of Tim's cockerel's, in determined-looking mood!

Life-changing chooks

The Lights are always willing to help Sue with the weeding!

Getting their first hens heralded something of a lifestyle revolution for Mike and Sue Woolnough – this is their story

Most of you reading this will keep chickens as pets that have a useful by-product, namely eggs. Some of you will keep and breed birds for showing. A few of you may even eat the unwanted cockerels that your breeding programme produces. But I wonder how many of you started out with poultry purely for their meat and eggs? That's exactly what we did.

Sue and I had been vegetarian for several years, having become very disillusioned with the way commercial meat was produced. Then, after reading bad things about supermarket fruit and vegetables, we decided that the time was right to aim for self-sufficiency.

Good times

So, in August 2004, we took on a local allotment; on the edge of a big housing estate. Soon afterwards we obtained our first two chickens for the garden. We'd read every chicken book we could find to help with breed choice, and opted for Light Sussex as they are utility birds and have a gentle nature. We wanted eggs, of course, but also planned to breed for meat if everything went smoothly.

As it turned out, though, we got off to a terrible start, having been sold sick birds. In our naïvety, we didn't realise that we shouldn't have accept them. As a consequence, the original two died, but not before spreading sickness to their successors. One of our first newly-acquired skills was the ability to give antibiotic injections to chickens! We had to do this morning and night, and found that the easiest way was to take the birds off their roosts in the dark, when they are sleepy and easier to handle. We certainly had some late nights and early

the allotment. We used half of the existing old shed, adding a 20'x10' run on the side using strong posts and chicken wire. Because we couldn't get over there morning and night to let them in and out, we had to make it fox-proof. Chicken wire was used right across the top to prevent foxes jumping over the sides and in; it was weaved carefully into the sides so there were no gaps. Then, to prevent them from digging their way inside, we dug out the soil inside to a depth of about a foot, covered the area with chain-link fencing, wired this securely to the sides and then replaced all the soil.

Two-legged attacks

Unfortunately, when you keep chickens on an allotment, their housing has to be strong enough to withstand attacks from two-legged as well as four-legged predators. But, apart from a couple of vandal attacks, we have been lucky so far and, when one of our sheds was broken into, the wind actually blew the door shut again so the birds didn't escape. They would quickly have been lost to foxes, as several have been seen on the allotments, and one family even dug out an earth on the vacant plot next to ours.

Both birds from the first hatch turned out to be males, and thus provided our first experience of chooks for the pot. Killing them was a rather horrific experience, as the hand-held despatcher we used came with no instructions, and we didn't get it right. Our whole philosophy has been that we'll only eat meat when the animal has had a good life; been treated well then killed quickly and humanely. We felt that we had let the birds down badly. We then tried the broom-handle method, and quickly learned the grisly meaning of the saying 'flapping around like a headless chicken!' Although it was messy and unpleasant, we did at least know that the bird was instantly dead. Lots of advice from the *Practical Poultry* forum followed and, eventually, we mastered the tricky job of using the despatcher. Now it's a fairly routine job, as is plucking and dressing the birds.

The taste of home-grown chicken is wonderful, particularly if

We use deep layers of leaves in our runs; they are topped-up regularly.

mornings while we were dealing with that crisis.

We were also sold a poultry house that was entirely unsuitable for large fowl – especially the huge rooster that we eventually bought. The lesson must be for all beginners to take as much independent advice as possible before getting involved with poultry. Don't rely on the advice you're given by anybody who is trying to sell you something! If you have access to the Internet, then you've got the perfect place to start – the *Practical Poultry* forum. So many people there are very helpful; you'll get a variety of experience-based opinions, but also a framework on which to base a decision.

Despite these early setbacks, we persisted and started hatching. We borrowed a small incubator from a friend, and bought six eggs from an online auction. Two hatched, and we were hooked. We bought our own incubator and built a run on

Newly-hatched Light Sussex chicks. Note the use of healing crystals in their drinking water

you give them plenty of fresh greens to eat as we do. Our chickens are our two legged composting bins – virtually all the greenery and weeds from the allotment get fed to them. Nothing the supermarkets sell can compare, both for birds and eggs, and we include the so-called free-range chickens in that.

We loved the nature of the Sussex, and we so fell in love with chickens that our flock grew very quickly. The intention was to sell hatching eggs and pullets, and eat the cockerels. Some beautiful buffs, then speckled, and eventually silvers, browns and reds, all in large fowl, plus light, speckled and buff bantams, all joined our burgeoning flock. The runs on the allotment expanded at an amazing rate. We discovered a new way of building them, using the 12-foot long sections of steel-wired panels used for security fencing on building sites. A wide trench was dug all round the perimeter then wire netting was buried to stop foxes digging their way in. The tops were covered over with nylon trawler fishing netting after we managed to buy a huge bale of the stuff. Adapted second-hand garden sheds made up the 'Chook Hilton' accommodation. It looks rather like we are building our own shanty town – virtually the whole of one plot is chicken housing.

Leaf litter

All our runs are floored with a deep layer of autumn leaves, which the council deliver to our allotments by the truckload when they clear them from the park. We have a large pen to hold the leaves in, and use them by the barrowful in the runs, and even inside the houses. The birds absolutely love scratching around in them, especially as we regularly add handfuls of corn into the mix; it keeps them happily occupied for hours! The most important advantage is that the leaves stop the runs from turning into swampland after rain. Also, the whole lot eventually breaks down into some wonderful compost that we can spread over the vegetable beds.

With Avian Influenza always lurking just over the horizon, we've bought several rolls of wild bird-

Mike admiring his unusual, honey-coloured Coronation Sussex

proof netting that we can fix all round the perimeter of our runs, and tarpaulins that will stretch over the top. So, if we're asked to bring our birds 'indoors', then we'll be ready, although we've no intention of doing so until required to.

Our rapid expansion brought us another run-in with disease. We bought some birds and, very foolishly, didn't isolate them before mixing them with our other stock. Mycoplasma reared its ugly head, and we were back to the vet, and giving the birds injections again. While Sue, who isn't altogether comfortable with handling the birds, was restraining our large cockerel Hagrid on the living room table one night, I stuck the needle in. But I must have hit a nerve because he reacted badly. She held on gamely as he squawked, flapped and struggled, all the time with a syringe sticking out of his chest. We'd broken the golden rule and caused a lot of unnecessary work and stress because of it. New birds must be isolated!

We've tried other breeds too;

buff Orpingtons, a colourful mixture of Wyandottes, and even the odd Pekin by mistake. But our hearts belonged to Sussex. We soon had nearly 100 birds, but realised that things were getting a little out of hand. We're not officially allowed to have cockerels on the allotments, although several other plot holders do, and the Field Secretary turns a blind eye. But, with our 20 or so males crowing their little heads off, people were beginning to take notice. Something had to be done; space for the growers was getting short.

So, with heavy hearts, we decided that the flock needed to be reduced. Our favourites – by a long way – were the buff Sussex bantams. These friendly, inquisitive and endearing little birds capture your heart if you let them! We generally only have four people at most for Sunday dinner, and a nice plump bantam provides more than enough meat for everyone. We also decided to keep a reduced number of large fowl Lights, as they were the variety that we started with, plus we had some top-quality stock. We have a beautiful and rare large Coronation pullet too that we have great hopes for, as well as a small flock of speckled bantams. Our plans now are to have a small, mixed-colour flock of Sussex bantams, and keep a cockerel or two, depending on which variety we fancy breeding that season.

Coronation beauties

We're fascinated by the gene that passes on the Coronation colouring, and recently hatched some chicks from a Coronation father, that we subsequently realised is carrying the gold gene, matched with splash hens. Some of the young have turned out to be the most beautiful honey colour, with white neck hackles. It will be very interesting to see what their adult plumage looks like.

We found that chickens which free-range in the garden add that certain indefinable something. Ours have given us hours of pleasure with the comical things they get up to. Be warned, however, that they can very quickly destroy your beautifully landscaped and planted pride and joy. We found that three large fowl are more than capable

Mating a buff Sussex cockerel to a Light hen produces sex-linked youngsters – all girls will be pure-bred buffs, while the boys will be Lights carrying the gold gene and, hence, are only suitable for the oven

of decimating most plant life in an average-sized garden. But three bantams are far less destructive, while still keeping pests like grubs and caterpillars down completely.

Nevertheless, we eventually tired of living in a giant chicken run, and recently moved all our stock on to the allotments. We're very pleased to have the garden back, and feel sure it'll eventually recover from the depredations of the chickens. On the other hand, we're not troubled by Lily Beetle now, but we don't have any lilies either!

We were badly affected by the awful red mite epidemic that seemed to hit just about everybody a few years ago. Some of our sheds are very old, and they got absolutely riddled with the pest – to plague proportions. The only way we have found to keep them under some sort of control is to spray thoroughly with a strong solution of Jeyes fluid – once a week if necessary. The problems with red mite have made us turn our thoughts in another direction. Everybody tells us that waterfowl aren't prone to attack from these little horrors, so we're planning to get some ducks soon. Once again, we're researching frantically, and

asking the advice of everybody we know who keeps them. They have to be utility birds, not too noisy or aggressive in case we end up keeping any at home, and we don't want birds that look like wild Mallards as we'll be accused of pinching them from the park! It's going to be a difficult choice.

On the self-sufficiency front, we've made huge progress, and now eat entirely our own soft fruit and vegetables, only buying things that we can't realistically produce ourselves such as bananas and cereals. Our 'patch' has expanded to a nice block of four allotments that total a quarter of an acre. In

Early days at 'Chook Corner'

our first year we grew more than 60 varieties of vegetables and soft fruit, and their taste was a revelation. We plan to use one of the new plots as an orchard, and have started planting it with fruit trees of all sorts.

We're trying to stick to traditional old British varieties, and have just enjoyed our first harvest; a lovely Discovery apple. The chooks are allowed out into it when we are working over there. Their runs were very quickly denuded of any trace of greenery, so this is a nice way to supplement their diet. They probably get plenty of protein from the many grubs and insects they root out, and help to keep pests under control a little. They are easily lured back home with a 'magical' handful of corn.

The chickens were certainly 'stepping stones' to a different way of life for us, and led to so many other changes. Sue cooks all our bread and biscuits, we make our own wine and only rarely use our car now as we cycle wherever possible – even doing our weekly supermarket run by bike armed with pannier bags and backpacks.

So, be warned... chickens can change your lives! ●